COMPLETE GUIDE TO GASOLINE MARINE ENGINES

JOHN FLEMING

Editor: John P. O'Connor, Jr.

Bristol Fashion Publications
Harrisburg, Pennsylvania

Complete Guide To Gasoline Marine Engines -- *John Fleming*

Published by Bristol Fashion Publications

ISBN: 1-892216-30-2
LCCN: 00-131362

Contribution acknowledgments

Inside Graphics: By the author or as noted
Cover Design: John P. Kaufman
Cover Photo: Mercury Marine

DEDICATION

I dedicate this book to my wife, Doris Fleming, without whom the world would be a darker place and none of these words would ever have been written. For 47 years she has been my inspiration. With her help all things are possible.

INTRODUCTION

Marine engines are really rather simple devices, if we will only let them be so. Yes, there are complicated things going on in our engines, but even those need not be a mystery. This book will bring everything you ever wanted to know about the four-stroke marine engine down to an understandable level.

The modern marine engine is an abstract type of contraption with two distinct faces. On one hand, we have a basic engine that has not changed a great deal for many years. Many of the principles on which it operates are as old as Sir Isaac Newton.

On the other hand, we have a set of electronic systems as new as today. The electronic systems on our engines have been both a blessing and a curse. They have allowed us to do some astonishing things with the engine, but they have also given us some headaches during their development.

I view the engine at three levels. That very basic engine we have had for so many years is the first level. The electronic suite that serves the systems on the engine is the second level and the sometimes uneasy marriage between the two is the third level.

On the first level, this book will detail the important mechanical parts of the engine. It will further tell you what the engine does and how it accomplishes these task. It will also describe some of the more important recent changes to engines.

On the second level, it will describe the operation of electronic engine systems and explain in general terms the benefits electronic controls offer to the engine builder.

It will not delve deeply into electronic circuitry because we cannot repair an electronic module at the shop level. We use a laptop computer to diagnose the problems when our electronics fail, but we are limited to replacement of the entire module as a remedy.

A good general understanding of the module's function is important, but if you are interested in electronics for their own sake you must look elsewhere.

At the third level, we will consider the manner in which electronic engine systems fit into the overall operation of the engine. Instant and precise control of the ever-changing requirements of the engine is the forte of the electronics package.

Please do not let the matter of electronics daunt you. Too many people have thrown up their hands and said, "I don't understand." Then they simply quit. There is a limited amount you must understand to deal with the engine.

Each level will be addressed in separate sections and each section will have a gradually increasing degree of sophistication. You can read as far as you wish into any area or chapter of this book, then stop.

You can pick up at another chapter and proceed. I hope you will read it all and be encouraged to look for other books on the subject.

John Fleming

TABLE OF CONTENTS

CHAPTER ONE

ENGINE STRUCTURE

For the genesis of this subject, let us consider the major parts of the marine engine. We will give them names and a short description of their function so we know exactly what is intended by any given term you may encounter in this book.

Using this chapter as a reference will keep us on the same track.

The engine uses two basic assemblies, the cylinder block and cylinder head(s). If the engine were a house, the cylinder block would be the foundation. Everything in or on the engine is tied to or supported by the cylinder block.

The cylinder block is usually cast from iron or aluminum, although few marine engine blocks have been cast from aluminum because of the effects of salt corrosion and electrolysis caused by seawater. Engines cast of aluminum must be freshwater cooled.

The cylinder block will provide a structure for the cylinder bores, which are cylindrical receptacles that hold the pistons. Gasoline-fueled, marine engines employ 1, 2, 3, 4, 6 or 8 cylinders in various patterns. Diesel engines may have many more.

The cylinders may be "in line," which means exactly what the name implies, or they may be in a "V" configuration. Engines with cylinders cast as a V may have different angles to the V and this affects the engine operation.

Later we will discuss the balance of the engine and other features of engine operation affected by the angle of the cylinders to the crankshaft.

The cylinder block is surrounded by water passages that cast into the block. The coolant that maintains engine temperature is circulated here. The design of these passages and the flow patterns are controlled by various types of gaskets.

Because engine makers do not agree on how the coolant should be circulated, various engines will have different flow patterns. These patterns are designed to prevent hot spots in the engine.

Another series of holes drilled into the block distributes lubricating oil to the various parts of the engine. These holes are called oil passages, and the series of passages constitutes the oil gallery.

Oil is fed into this gallery by the lubricating oil pump. As it moves through the engine, the oil both cools and lubricates. Marine engines employ an oil cooler that is, in effect, a heat exchanger cooled by sea water. This keeps the oil temperature at the proper level.

The top of the cylinder block is called the deck and the bottom of the block is called the base. The main bearing housings are at the base of the block. The bottom halves of these housings resemble stirrups and they are bolted onto the base of the block.

These lower halves of the main bearing housings are called main bearing caps and may be either cast from iron or forged from steel. The crankshaft runs in a set of bearings held in the main bearing housings.

Inside the block may be a series of scantlings, cast into the structure for stiffening. These are raised ribs called webbings where the metal is thicker. There are also stiffening ribs called that support the main bearing housings.

A seal at each end of the engine prevents the

lubricating oil from running out of the engine. These seals are referred to as a main bearing seal (rear) and timing cover seal (front of the engine.)

Crankshafts themselves may also be cast from iron or forged from steel. They have an offset arm that provides the leverage to turn the crankshaft. That offset arm makes it possible for the crankshaft to turn reciprocating motion into rotary motion.

The crankshaft has a set of pins or journals. The pins to which the connecting rods are affixed are called rod journals, while those that support the crankshaft in the block are called crank pins.

The connecting rod links the piston to the crankshaft, transferring pressure from the piston to the crankshaft arm. There will be one connecting rod for each piston. These rods have small ends and big ends.

The big end circles the rod journals while the small end circles the wrist pin, which attaches the connecting rod to the piston. It sits transversely (across) to the piston and the point at which the wrist pin is affixed to the piston is called the wrist pin boss.

Bearings for the wrist pin may be in the piston only, or they may be in the connecting rod only. On some pistons there are bearings in both the piston and the connecting rod. These systems are called full floating wrist pins.

Pistons themselves are aluminum castings that resemble an abbreviated can with the bottom missing. They ride in the cylinder bores and accept the pressure from the burned gasses the engine generates.

Piston rings circle the piston and ride in grooves, which are machined to close tolerances, about the circumference of the piston. The area around the top of the groove is called a land.

Thus we have piston rings riding in lands and grooves. The piston rings are of two types: compression rings and oil scraper rings. Both take up the space between the piston and the cylinder walls, yet they serve two separate purposes.

Compression rings hold the burned gasses on top of the piston and separate them from the crankcase. Oil scraper rings literally scrape the lube oil off the cylinder walls and maintain it in the crankcase. This ring contact with the cylinder walls also dissipates heat from the piston surfaces.

Though they are closely fit, the piston rings will eventually begin to wear, those small clearances will increase and compression will be lost, oil will be burned and the engine will suffer. The parts must be replaced.

The four-stroke engine employs a camshaft, which is a strange-looking metal shaft with eccentrics or bumps along its length. These bumps are called lobes, and the part that rides upon these lobes is called a cam follower, or lifter.

The cam follower is raised and lowered by the lobes when the camshaft rotates. The camshaft is driven by a cam gear or timing gear and/or a timing chain at the front of the engine. The camshaft rides in cam bearings supported by the cam journals.

There are two lobes for each cylinder, one for the intake and one for the exhaust valve(s). An extra lobe on the front of the camshaft, near the timing gear, operates the mechanical fuel pump on engines that are so equipped.

The camshaft may be in the block or in the cylinder head. Camshafts in the cylinder block are called cam-in-block and, on modern engines, they are always single shafts. Camshafts in the cylinder head are called overhead cams.

Overhead cam systems are rarely found on the inboard engines of today but they are common on four-stroke, outboards. The overhead camshaft is very efficient. It rides atop the cylinder head, where it also is driven by a timing chain, timing gear or timing belt.

The overhead cam may be single or double. The single overhead camshaft (SOHC) employs a rocker arm, just as the cam-in-block engine does. This single camshaft operates both intake and exhaust valves.

The double overhead camshaft (DOHC) employs two shafts, one for the intake valves and one for the exhaust valves. This is the most efficient system in use today. The DOHC head needs no rocker arms, no push rods and no separate cam follower. A cup encircles the valve stem and the camshaft rides directly upon this cup.

Cylinder heads are major castings that cover the tops of the cylinders and close them off from the outside air. The combustion chamber is inside the cylinder head. Valve guides machined or pressed into the cylinder heads support the valves that admit or stop the flow of gasses into or out of the engine.

A valve has a circular head, or top end, and a thin, cylindrical stem, or tail, sticking out. The head has a face onto which a seat is machined. This valve seat has an angle that matches another seat machined into the cylinder head. Together they control the flow of gasses into and out of the cylinder.

Over the years, these seats will be worn or burned and then they will fail to seal. This decreases compression and performance. The valves and their seats will require regrinding to restore that seal and performance.

The valves are pushed open by the rocker arms on a cam-in-block engine. The camshaft rotates, the cam followers rise and fall, a push rod operates the rocker arm. A valve spring coiled about the valve stem returns the valve to its seat.

Rocker arms resemble handles that you see on an old hand-style water pump. The head supports a set of rocker studs that, in turn, hold the rocker arms with a ball/socket mount. The push rod pushes against one side of the rocker arm and the rocker arm applies pressure to the valve stem on the other side.

Cylinder heads have a combustion chamber machined or cast into the surface that faces the cylinder bore. This combustion chamber is where gasses are generated by burning fuel. The roof or top of this chamber holds the seats against which the valves are seated.

The shape and size of this combustion chamber is

important. The size controls the compression ratio of the engine, while the shape has much to do with how the fuel burns inside the cylinder. We will devote a chapter to combustion chamber design.

The cylinder head receives a great deal of pressure when the engine fires. The number is in the hundreds of pounds. The head is retained atop the cylinder with a set of head bolts or head studs.

Head studs are threaded into the block with coarse or standard threads. Nuts that are used on head studs have fine or S.A.E. threads. All of these fastenings are high-tensile steel to withstand both the pressure and the vibration of the engine.

Figure 1

The head studs are shown protruding from the cylinder block.

A cylinder head gasket seals the joint between the cylinder head and cylinder block. Head gaskets, which must accept great heat and pressure, are made of high-tech materials that vary from gasket maker to gasket maker.

The intake manifold is on the side of the cylinder head on an in-line engine and between the cylinder banks on V block engines. It has a series of pipes and passages that conduct the new air/fuel charge to the cylinders.

The exhaust manifolds are bolted to the sides of the cylinders on all engines. They receive the burned gasses, at high temperature, from the cylinder and conduct them outward. Both intake and exhaust manifolds are the subject of extensive research and we will spend a good deal of time with them later. The next chapter will describe the most elementary view of how the engine runs and why it runs, but before we leave this area I want to say a word about metals.

The metallurgy of the engine is highly complex because so many attributes are required from the numerous parts and pieces. For example, piston rings on the 5.7 MerCruiser engine, turning 3,000 rpms, are traveling up and down the cylinder bore at a speed of 1,740 feet per minute. Every three minutes that you operate the engine, those rings are dragged across the cylinder walls for a distance of more than a mile.

They do this hour after hour, year after year, at high temperatures. This is truly a marvelous bit of metal to accept that kind of punishment and survive for so long. Similar stories could be told about the other parts of your engine.

CHAPTER TWO

ENGINE FUNCTION

We have told you what the engine looks like and the general layout of the parts. This mechanical wonder was designed and built at considerable expense, so it must have a purpose. What does it do?

The marine engine burns a chemical fuel inside the cylinder; thus it is an internal-combustion engine. It uses a piston that reciprocates, that is to say, it moves backward and forward or up and down. Thus it is also a reciprocating-piston engine.

That downward motion of the piston is caused by expanding gasses that are created as the fuel burns inside the cylinder.

The piston is driven downward and the connecting rod transfers this force to the crankshaft. The crankshaft begins to turn and we have power available. Now let us see what we have actually accomplished.

We have taken a chemical fuel and changed it into heat energy, by burning. We have changed that energy into reciprocating motion and reciprocating motion into rotary motion. The force that we created by burning the fuel is now available to us in a usable form.

Let's take a much closer look at how it accomplishes this.

All marine engines can be separated into four

categories. Two are based upon cyclic operations, two-stroke or four-stroke, and two are defined by fuel type, gasoline or diesel.

Because the four-stroke engine operates upon the same principles whether inboard, outboard or stern drive, we won't separate them. This book will address four-cycle engine principles only.

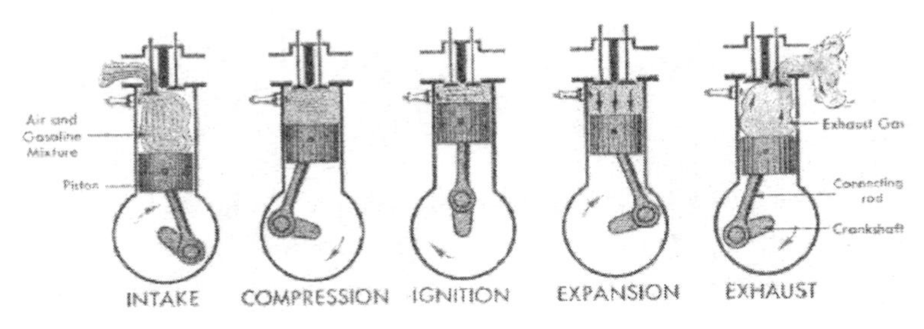

Figure 2

The five stages of a four stoke engine.

FOUR-STROKE ENGINES

Gasoline fueled, four-stroke engines employ four separate strokes of the piston, which occur during two revolutions of the crankshaft to complete a single cycle. The four strokes are called, in order, intake, compression, power and exhaust. This system is sometimes referred to as the Otto cycle in honor of its inventor.

What happens during each of these strokes? Begin with the intake stroke. The engine is at top dead center (TDC) and the piston is at its upper limit. The intake valve is open. On that first stroke, the piston moves downward and pressure drops inside the cylinder.

As the pressure falls below atmospheric, the air/fuel mix is forced into the cylinder. When the piston reaches bottom dead center (BDC), the intake stroke is complete and a fresh charge of air/fuel mix is in place.

The intake valve will close and the piston will begin to move upward. This is the compression stroke. On this stroke, the fresh charge is compressed and heated in the cylinder. As the piston nears top dead center on the compression stroke, we get a spark.

The spark must come at the proper time and the engine only fires once on every second revolution. Optimum timing for that spark varies with a number of factors we will not try to describe at this time but will certainly revisit at several points in this book.

The fuel is ignited and the piston is driven downward, imparting pressure to the crankshaft as it goes. This is the power stroke and, of course, it is this power that we seek. Just before the piston reaches bottom dead center on the power stroke, the exhaust valve will open.

This permits the last of the pressure from burned gasses to aid the removal of the exhaust from the engine. When the piston begins to move upward again, we are on the exhaust stroke. This is the fourth and final stroke, after which we begin again.

THE DIESEL DIFFERENCE

The four-stroke diesel engine operates on the same four strokes but varies in operation in several notable ways. The first of these is the matter of compression. When gasses are compressed, they are heated by that pressure. The faster they are compressed, the hotter they become.

Also, the greater the pressure, the greater the temperature. The diesel engine generates much higher compression pressure than does a gasoline engine.

On the intake stroke, the diesel receives only air.

On the compression stroke, the diesel engine generates very high pressures indeed and the cylinder is heated to elevated temperatures. On the power stroke the diesel gets no spark like the gasoline engine does; it only gets fuel from an injector.

The fuel is injected into the cylinder at extreme pressure. Ignition is caused by the heat that is already in the cylinder, raised by compression. This gives rise to another term, compression ignition. In simple language, the engine fires because the air in the cylinder is very hot.

The diesel varies in operation from the gasoline engine in at least one other important way. The diesel injector pump generates enough pressure to keep on spraying fuel into the cylinder after the fuel is first ignited. This gives meaning to the term constant pressure.

The diesel engine is a constant-pressure engine because the injector continues to feed fuel to the cylinder throughout much of the power stroke. The gasoline engine draws a single volume of air/fuel mix and fires that. Thus, it is a constant-volume engine.

This steady push against the diesel piston is in stark contrast to the sometimes violent pop of the gasoline engine and is the true heart of the difference between these engines.

Let us review briefly. For the gasoline-fueled engine, think of four strokes. On the intake stroke, we draw a single charge of air/fuel mix. On the compression stroke, we compress the mixture. On the power stroke, we ignite the entire fuel/air mix with a spark.

Also on the power stroke, we burn that volume of air/fuel mix entirely, at one time. The pressure generated rises rapidly but is of fairly short duration.

For the diesel engine, think also of four strokes. On the intake stroke, we draw a volume of air alone, with no fuel involved. On the compression stroke, we compress this air to extreme pressures and temperatures. On the power stroke, we inject fuel into the cylinder.

The fuel is ignited by heated air and the piston begins to move downward on the power stroke. The injector continues to spray fuel into the cylinder for a portion of this downward travel, maintaining pressure on the piston.

Every person who has taken an interest in engines has at one time or another heard the term "timing". This is generally understood by those who work on gasoline engines as the point at which the spark plug fires.

The diesel engine has a timing point that is controlled by the fuel injector. When the injector begins to spray, the fuel begins to burn. The injector pump times the power impulse for the engine.

When you have these principles straight in your head, you already understand a few things that many mechanics do not.

CHAPTER THREE

ENGINE MECHANICS

In the first two chapters we learned to identify the parts of the engine and generally how the engine operates. Now let us learn to measure the engine itself and quantify the work it does. Begin with the size or capacity of the engine.

The capacity of the engine is the same as its displacement. It is a product of the bore and stroke of a single cylinder, multiplied by the number of cylinders and expressed in cubic measure.

The bore is the diameter of any cylinder while the stroke is the distance that a piston moves during a single rotation of the crankshaft. Cubic displacement for a single cylinder is the amount of air that would be displaced by the movement of a piston from bottom dead center to top dead center.

Think of a soda can. The top of the can is the piston at top dead center. The bottom of the can is the piston at bottom dead center. The diameter of the can is the bore. The height of the can is the stroke. The sides of the can are the cylinder bores.

The total contents of the can, expressed in cubic measure, is the displacement of the cylinder. Multiply this figure by the number of cylinders and you have total displacement for the engine.

There is a simple formula for this computation:

B x B x S x .785 x N = D

In this formula we see that Bore x Bore x Stroke x .785 x The Number of Cylinders equals cubic Displacement. For this computation, let us use an engine of known capacity to test our formula.

Try an 8-cylinder, 350 cubic-inch block with a 4-inch bore and a 3.48-inch stroke. We have 4 x 4 x 3.48 x .785 x 8 = 349.67 cubic inches of displacement. That is close enough for government work.

For many years, we gave the displacement of our engines in cubic inches. In time we changed to liters or fractions thereof. We did this to better agree with the international community that bought ever-greater numbers of our engines.

How can we compare liters and cubic inches? A liter equals 60.023 cubic inches. If we multiply 5.7 liters by 60.023 cubic inches we only get 342.13 cubic inches. Obviously that does not really match the figures for our MerCruiser engine very closely.

We all know that the true figure is almost 350 cubic inches but the error is introduced in the conversion and in advertising considerations. Why is cubic displacement important? It is the best indication of an engine's potential to develop power.

Power is the ability to do work. How do we measure power? The commonly recognized unit is horsepower. A horsepower is defined as 33,000 foot pounds of work produced each minute. Note the amount of work and the element of time. This will become very important to our discussion.

There can be no discussion of horsepower without some reference to torque. Surely the two are inseparable, when the piston engine is involved. They go together like white and rice but many people do not understand just which one is the rice.

Torque is defined as twisting moment, but I want you to recognize exactly what that means. Torque is a little-understood product of engine operation. Torque is a potential and torque, of itself, does not do any work.

I can hear the howls, yet this is true. Torque alone will not move a boat or lift a weight. Torque is measured in foot-pounds, (written lbs./ft.) and the nature of torque is easily understood.

To any shaft, attach a 1-foot lever. To that lever apply a 1-pound weight or force, exactly 12 inches from the centerline. You now have 1 foot-pound of torque. The lever is known as an arm and it may be more or less than 1 foot long.

The lever that is longer or shorter than 1 foot is not a problem. Measure the length of the lever and convert that measurement to fractions of a foot. Multiply the answer by the weight applied to the lever, expressed in pounds or fractions thereof. The result is lbs./ft of potential. As an example:

A 6-inch lever or arm is 1/2 foot long. A 10-pound weight applied to that lever will produce 5 lbs./ft. of torque. But the shaft has not moved. It has done no work.

As soon as the shaft begins to move against a load, the effect is measured as horsepower, or fractions thereof. There is a formula that expresses this quite well:

$$\text{Tq x rpms / 5252 = Horsepower}$$

In this formula, Torque (Tq) x Revolutions Per Minute (rpms) divided by the constant 5252 = Horsepower. Again, note the element of time (revolutions per minute).

Let us run that 350 cubic-inch engine through this formula. It is rated at 260 horsepower at 4,450 rpm. Torque is given at 305 lbs./ft. Now multiply 305 lbs./ ft. of torque by 4,450 RPM's and we get a figure of 1,357,250. Divide by the constant 5,252 and we get 258.425 horsepower. Again, close enough.

Keep in mind the elements of torque. A pressure or

force, applied to a lever or arm, operating around a shaft. Heat generated by fuel burning in the cylinder creates the needed pressure or force. That pressure is applied to the piston top and thence to the crankshaft arm. It operates in a circular motion, around the crankshaft center,

When the force hits the crankshaft, we have torque. When the engine begins to move, we have horsepower. Nothing could be simpler. Pressure produces torque and is then turned into horsepower by the rotating crankshaft.

We can tailor torque output with a transmission and we can adjust the delivered torque periodically by changing gears. Yet the marine engine has no gear change, and therein lies the principal reason why it must have a broad torque band.

Those principles are the essentials of operation for any piston engine. It is obvious that much is happening simultaneously and in a proper sequence when the engine operates.

Much has been said about the cubic displacement of our engines and it would be good to understand why displacement is important. □As we have seen, the elements of displacement are bore, stroke and number of cylinders. □Let us take each and weigh the effect of size.

Again, use that 350 cubic-inch engine. Remember, there was a 4 inch bore. A piston with a diameter of 4 inches will have a surface area of 12.567 square inches.

The calculation is quite simple. Use this formula:

$$A = Pi \times R^2$$

Here A equals piston area in square inches, Pi equals 3.1416 and the radius equals 2 inches (1/2 the bore). Square the radius and multiply by the value 3.1416 for Pi. The result rounds out at about 12.567 square inches.

Let us now burn a chemical fuel in the cylinder and develop a considerable amount of pressure inside. We'll assume a pressure of 50 lbs/in.^{2} from that burning fuel.

Multiply 50 lbs./in.^{2} x 12.567 inches and we get 628.35 pounds of force on the piston top. Obviously, the more square inches of piston surface we have, the greater will be the total force. Add to that surface and you increase the force on the crankshaft arm.

For example, let us increase that bore to 5 inches. The radius is now 2.5 inches, the square of that figure is 6.25 and the figure for Pi is still 3.1416. Our piston top now has an area of 19.635 square inches, about a 50 percent increase for only a 1 inch increase in diameter.

More importantly, our same cylinder pressure of 50 lbs./in.^{2} will produce a total force of 981.75 pounds. That too is roughly a 50 percent increase in total pressure for a 25 percent increase in cylinder bore.

For this next example, let us go back to the actual dimensions of our engine.

What is going to happen to that force we developed by applying pressure to the piston top? The connecting rod will transfer it to the crankshaft arm.

The connecting rod cannot transfer all of the pressure from piston to crankshaft. They are joined at an angle and the amount of force applied to the crank arm will vary with the angle of the connecting rod and the angle of the crankshaft arm.

It will always be less than 100 percent, and this loss is one of the inefficiencies of a piston engine. Just for the sake of this discussion, however, assume that we could achieve 100 percent transfer.

Remember, our 350 cubic-inch engine has a 3.48-inch stroke. Remember also, the piston travels two ways, up and down, to get that much stroke. The arm or lever on the crankshaft must then be half the length of the stroke, say 1.74 inches or 0.145 feet.

Multiply that 628.35 pounds of pressure by the 0.145 feet and we get 91.11 lbs./ft. of torque. What if the stroke were increased to 4 inches? We now have a 2-inch arm. This is

0.167 feet and the torque is increased to 104.93 lbs./ft.

We increased the length of our arm or lever by 15 percent and we got a 15 percent increase in torque. Increase the bore or stroke of the engine and the displacement will increase. Total pressure on the piston will increase and the effort applied to the crank arm will increase.

At the same time, if the stroke is increased, the crank arm becomes longer and the torque developed will increase accordingly. Sounds easy, right? Why not just put a nice long arm on that crankshaft, stretch out the stroke and really add to the torque figures.

At first blush, that sounds like a great idea, but the problem lies in a thing that we call “kinetic energy”.

That piston moves up and down. It stops at the top of the stroke and starts again. It stops at the bottom of the stroke and starts again. Thus, we have two starts and two stops for every revolution of the crankshaft. The piston is subject to the effects of inertia.

Inertia has two components. The first is the tendency of a body at rest to remain at rest until it is acted upon by a greater force. The second is the tendency of a body in motion to continue in motion until acted upon by a greater force.

The effort to make these starts and stops of the piston must be accomplished against the forces of inertia and the effort to do this causes a considerable loss of energy. That loss can be described as inertia energy loss, and it is substantial.

Inertia losses can be increased dramatically by adding weight to the piston or length to the stroke. The engine designer must weigh size against efficiency. Cubic inches are a definite advantage if total horsepower is your goal. They may become a burden if efficiency is the main consideration.

We will go into greater detail in the chapter covering rotating assemblies, but for now, suffice to say, the effort to change linear motion of the piston into rotary motion of the crankshaft is a real problem.

CHAPTER FOUR

CARBURETORS

THE INDUCTION SYSTEM

The engine employs an induction system, which is used to induce air and fuel into the engine. This system, one of the most critical components of engine operation, consists of the carburetor or injector unit, intake manifold, cylinder heads, camshaft and valve train.

In this and the next few chapters, we will look at each of these parts individually, then see how they interact.

The carburetor is designed to mix air and gasoline -- or some other flammable fuel -- in pre-determined ratios. This device is rather simple in concept but may be more complex in its construction.

Gasoline, the most common fuel, burns ideally at ratios of 15 parts air to 1 part fuel, by weight. In other words, 15 pounds of air burned for each pound of fuel. If the weight of the air consumed is less than 15 parts to each part of fuel, the engine runs rich.

If the weight of the air consumed is greater than 15 parts to each part of fuel, the engine will run lean. Lean mixtures burn cleanly, but they run hot. Rich mixtures are dirty and produce more pollutants, but they run cooler.

High-efficiency power plants must run leaner while

high-performance power plants run richer mixtures. All engines must be richened up a bit at full throttle or they run the chance of mechanical failure. Lean mixtures can be run more easily at low to midrange speeds.

Let us discuss the parts of a carburetor and then we will move on to operation. The carburetor employs a body that is the skeleton on which it is built. The carburetor body is generally made of aluminum.

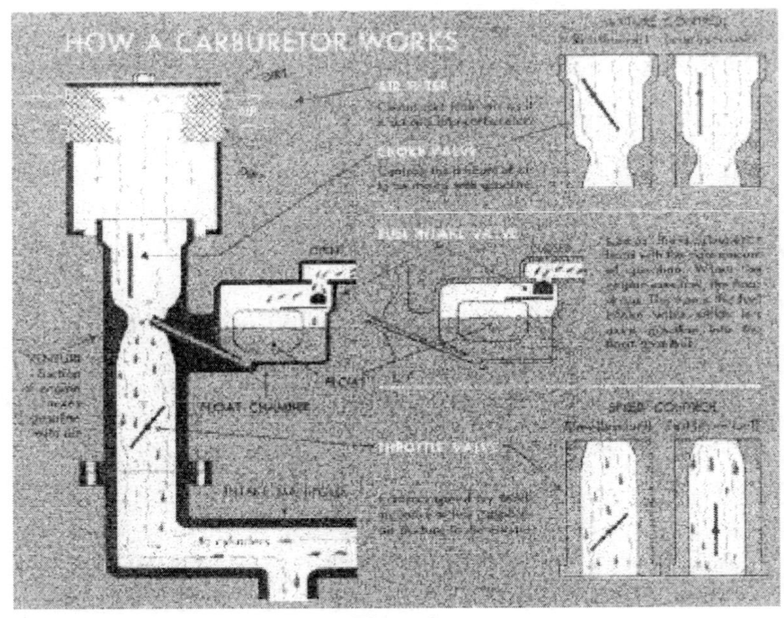

Figure 3

A simplified explanation of carburetor function.

Aluminum has its problems as a material for this purpose because it reacts to many salts, oxides and other chemicals, but it is light and easily cast. It is also easily drilled or machined and there are many passages in even a simple carburetor.

The body has one or more air passages cast into its

frame. The proper name for these passages is "throat". The throat is sometimes referred to as a barrel. Thus, we often hear the term "4-barrel carburetor" to describe a carburetor with 4 throats.

Each is equipped with an inner constriction called a venturi. Again, we often see the description "4-V carburetor" which denotes a carburetor with 4 venturis. This description should not create confusion if you keep in mind that there is one of each, one venturi for each throat on the carburetor body.

Thus, a 4-throat carburetor is also a 4-venturi carburetor. A carburetor may have one throat, or as many as the designer thinks is necessary. □Normally, there is a single throat for each cylinder or for each pair of cylinders.

The reason for this will become more apparent when we tackle this subject again in the chapter on induction systems.

The throats may be facing upward (vertically) or sideways (horizontally). The carburetor that feeds in a more or less vertical direction is called a down-draft carburetor, while the carburetor that feeds horizontally is called a side-draft carburetor.

The carburetor body also incorporates a bowl inside that is a float and a float valve. The float valve is often referred to as a needle and seat, in reference to its shape. The needle is shaped like a fat needle with a point that fits into the seat.

The float may be made of plastic, foam, sheet metal or cork and it does what the name implies: It floats in fuel. The float is cantilevered on a swing arm and the needle rides atop this arm. It may be retained by a small, light spring or it may simply sit in position.

The carburetor body has two butterflies for each throat. One is a throttle, and the other is a choke. The choke is upstream from the venturi. The throttle is downstream of the venturi.

Screwed into the body of the carburetor is one or more

jets. These are tubes with fixed-size orifices with one end in the carburetor bowl and the other ending in the venturi. They are generally made of brass.

Carburetors are fitted with an accelerator pump, which is attached to the throttle arm and operates in conjunction with it. Open the throttle and you activate the pump. Close the throttle and you prime it for the next stroke.

Atop the carburetor is a flash arrestor that resembles a hat across the tops of the throats. This flash arrestor is made of stainless steel and has a kind of gauze or a series of fins. It can save your life.

Carburetors vary from the simple to the truly exotic. I have skipped over at least two types of carburetor in this presentation. I have made no listing of parts for a pressure carburetor to burn gasses such as LP or LNG because we do not use pressurized gas fuels in a marine engine. I have also omitted a parts listing for slide valve or so called variable-venturi carburetors. These are seldom seen in marine applications except on two-stroke, racing engines.

The parts list for the carburetor is now complete. Let us see what each part does and how it accomplishes its purpose.

The carburetor depends upon moving air to make it work. The speed at which this air moves is critical to the efficiency of the carburetor.

Begin with a supply of fuel that is provided to the carburetor and delivered to the bowl. It enters through the float valve and begins to fill the bowl until finally the float begins to float upward against the float valve. As the bowl fills, the float valve is pressed into the seat, cutting off the flow of fuel at a predetermined level. As the engine demands fuel for its operation, the fuel level will diminish.

When the level drops, the float valve will be released and more fuel will be admitted to the bowl. This level will be maintained to close tolerances. If the float is too high or the float valve fails, the mixture of air and gas will become very rich and the engine may flood.

Let us assume that the float bowl is properly filled and we are going to start the engine. The choke butterfly is closed across the face of the throat. We may pump the throttle once or twice to activate the accelerator pump.

This gives us a shot of raw gas into the carburetor throat. We call this priming the engine. It richens the mixture to help start the engine. The choke is on, the engine is primed and we turn the switch key. The engine begins to turn over. The piston moves downward.

Air is forced into the carburetor throat and flows through the venturi. Pressure drops in the venturi and fuel begins to be drawn upward, from the bowl through the jets and into the moving air stream. This fuel is added to that from the accelerator pump.

The engine continues to rotate, the pressure continues to drop, and the flow velocity increases. Now this enriched mixture is delivered to the cylinder and the engine fires. Rotational speed increases dramatically after ignition.

As the engine rotates faster, more air flows down the carburetor throats. When the flow is fast enough, the pressure drop behind the venturis is substantial. Fuel is naturally drawn from the carburetor bowl and the engine will be able to operate on its own.

Do not forget that flash arrestor. The incoming air is passing through the arrestor and if we should get a backfire, it will catch the escaping gas and render the flames harmless. This is a vital piece of any marine engine.

Now, the choke opens and allows the carburetor to find its proper mixture level, dictated by the speed of the air flow in the venturi and the size of the jets. The faster the air flows down the carburetor throat and through the venturi, the more fuel will be drawn from the bowl.

Four concepts are at work here, and each is critical.

First, the speed of the flow in the throat/venturi is dictated by the amount of air flowing down the throat/venturi, vs. the diameter of the carburetor throat/venturi itself. The larger the carburetor throat/venturi, the slower will be the flow for a given volume of air.

Of course, a smaller throat/venturi will have a much faster flow velocity for the same volume of air. The flow speed for a given volume of air will vary in direct proportion to the number of square inches of area in the venturi itself.

Second, the speed of that flow controls the amount of pressure drop in the venturi. The faster the flow, the greater the pressure drop. The venturi reacts critically to flow speed.

A third consideration is this: The amount of fuel drawn from a given size jet will depend upon the speed of flow and the attendant pressure drop in the venturi. Speed up the flow of air and you draw more fuel through the jet. Slow it down and the fuel flow will decrease.

Fourth is the matter of fuel atomization or mixing. The faster the air flows through the carburetor throats, the better it will mix with the fuel droplets and the better the mixture will burn.

Do you see the dilemma? The engine is begging for air. It is pulling against the twin restrictions of throttle butterfly and venturi. If we make the carburetor throats larger and let in more air, we can get more horsepower and go faster, but what about the jets. They can only provide so much fuel.

The engine is going to lean out and that is really bad at the faster speeds, which we are now running. We could enlarge the throats/venturis anyway and get some more air.

But what if we slow down? Now the engine does not want so much air and the flow speed through the venturis has slowed way down. Those big, fat jets are flowing gobs of fuel the engine cannot use.

Moreover, the mixture of air and fuel in that slow-flowing air stream is very poor. The fuel does not atomize but goes down the carburetor throat in big drops, some of which settle out along the way. These drops puddle in the intake manifold and burn very poorly in the engine.

This is why the carburetor is always a compromise. If

you really want to go faster, you can enlarge the throat and flow more air through the carburetor. You will improve the high rpm performance, but the engine will not be happy idling around the docks.

You want better fuel efficiency? Reduce the number of throats or the size of the throats on your carburetor and you will see the fuel consumption go down. At the same time, you are going to lose the top end. The carburetor on your stock engine is a true compromise.

A great deal has been said in these pages about the size of the carburetor. What are some of the measurements we must recognize? Carburetors are measured in several ways. The principal measurements are flow capacities and venturi diameters.

Flow capacities are measured in cubic feet per minute (CFM). A common number for a 350 cubic-inch, 260 horsepower, marine engine is 600 CFM. Venturis are measured in inches of diameter. These diameters vary in size from one carburetor to another.

There may also be primary and secondary venturis in a single carburetor. These may not be the same size. The carburetor with unequal venturi diameters generally has small primary venturis and large secondary venturis.

The first thing many mechanics do when more performance is desired is install a larger CFM carburetor. If more economy is the goal, they reach for a smaller CFM unit. This is the easy way out, but it begs the question, "How much/little is enough?"

Remember, the factory that produced that engine had some pretty good engineers doing the design work. If you are going to improve upon what they have done, you should at least understand what you are about to undertake.

Any thorough discussion of carburetors and flow characteristics must include a recognition of the nature of pressure and what it means to the carburetor. Air pressure stands at 14.7 $lbs./in.^2$ at sea level. It will be reduced as altitude increases and increased as we drop below sea level.

Atmospheric pressure is exerted upon every single thing on this Earth, on a continuous basis. We will use atmospheric pressure as our zero line. Any pressure above atmospheric will be positive while any pressure below atmospheric will be negative.

Let's consider the operation of the engine. The piston goes down on the intake stroke and the pressure in the cylinder drops below atmospheric. We now have a negative pressure. Air from the outside is forced into the cylinder to fill the void.

To get there, it must flow through the carburetor throat. We are concerned with three aspects of that flow. How great is the pressure drop? How much air is going to flow through our venturi? How fast will it flow?

You do not have to be an engineer to understand this. The laws governing the operation of gasses in a pipe or gasses under pressure were written by two French scientists, Boyle and Charles. The laws are generally rather simple but quite sound.

We will refer to both Charles' Law and Boyle's Law throughout this book. You will find descriptions of each of these laws in any good encyclopedia. For the present discussion, suffice to say that, using these laws and data collected over a number of years, we have developed a series of flow charts that tell us that, at a given pressure, we can flow a known number of CFMs through an orifice (venturi) of a measured diameter. The engine, on the other hand, will demand a certain amount of air for each revolution, based upon its cubic displacement.

Our 350 cubic-inch engine will demand 175 cubic inches of air for each revolution. Remember, it only fires every other revolution. Thus it demands air for half the cylinders or 50 percent of its cubic displacement, every time it turns over.

Using the demand figure for each revolution, multiply by a given number of rpms and you have the demand or air requirement for any speed. We also know that we cannot deliver that full amount of air to the engine.

We must have some restriction in the venturi to pull fuel from the carburetor bowl. The volume of air we deliver, vs. the amount of demand the engine wants, expressed as a fraction, tells us the volumetric efficiency of the engine.

Now you are beginning to get down to the real essentials of carburetor sizes and designs.

Given these numbers, demand, flow speeds, jet sizes, etc., we can calculate essentially any facet of carburetor operation using the data available in the flow charts.

Once you feel you have a grasp of these principles, you are ready to go to a shop with a flow bench. This is a bench with a very sophisticated set of instruments that measures all those elements that we have described.

Offer to do whatever you have to. Work for nothing; do anything that does not break the law in return for instruction. Nothing you can learn about the operation of the engine will ever be more valuable to you than a good, sound understanding of induction systems.

CHAPTER FIVE

FUEL INJECTION

Fuel injectors do exactly what the name implies: They inject fuel, under pressure, into the engine's induction system. The fuel injector may be mechanical or electronic.

However, because there have been few fully mechanical fuel injection systems in use in this country, we will concern ourselves with electronic fuel-injection (EFI) units.

Electronic fuel injection actually uses mechanical parts with electronic controls. Control is the forte of the EFI unit.

Close, precise control of fuel, the amounts and the delivery times -- are possible. No other system even approaches it or offers the potential to integrate control of its function into an overall scheme.

There are two basic forms of the EFI unit for the four-stroke, gasoline-fueled engine: the throttle body injector (TBI) and the tuned port injector (TPI). The TPI is the most common system and we will concentrate on it.

The parts of any EFI unit are the fuel pump, the rail, and the injector itself. The entire unit is controlled by an electronic control module (ECM). The injector itself is actually an uncomplicated device, but the ECM is an entirely different animal.

The TPI is incorporated into the intake manifold, which we will cover later. For now, let us consider the parts

For the TPI, the injector itself has a body, which is generally tubular and is screwed into the intake manifold. Commonly, there is one injector for each port and they are located in the port runners.

The injector body ends in a pintle or nozzle. Just behind this nozzle, inside the body, is a spring-loaded valve that restricts the flow of fuel. On some types of injectors, this valve can be operated by applied pressure. On others it is operated by a solenoid

The intake manifold is the skeleton or support for the entire TPI unit, thus it has no body as does the carburetor. It does employ a butterfly to control the flow of air to the manifold and to the cylinders. This butterfly is located in an air box.

The air box may be fed by several intake runners, which are tubes with a tuned length. The entire assembly is called a ram-air intake, which we will cover in the chapter on integrated operation of induction systems.

A throttle body injector at first glance may be mistaken for a conventional carburetor. □The TBI unit uses a throttle body that is similar to a carburetor body. It sits atop the intake manifold and it has a throat or throats similar to those of a carburetor. There is no choke butterfly, but there is a butterfly for the throttle control.

The throttle arm on the injector system operates a throttle position sensor, an electronic element that tells the electronic control module the position of the throttle. The body of a TBI has no float bowl, no float or needle and seat arrangement. Rather, the TBI injector discharges into the throats on the throttle body.

The injector used for the throttle body injection is similar to the one used for the tuned port injector except for location.

Either system requires an electrically driven fuel pump to supply fuel to the injectors. There must be some type of fuel delivery device to bring fuel to the injectors. On the TPI system, we call this tube a rail.

The electronic control module (ECM) is the really sophisticated element in any injector system. It is the control element that makes it all work. A wiring harness connects it to the electronically controlled elements.

These are the parts of the EFI and they are few. Their operation is equally simple. The first consideration for the EFI unit is that it is not dependent upon any venturi or pressure differential to draw fuel from a carburetor bowl.

The nozzle provides fuel, under pressure and on demand. It can do this at any time or at any rpms. The ECM tells the injector when to deliver fuel, how much to deliver and at what interval to deliver it. The interval is referred to as spray time.

Spray time is the time, measured in fractions of a second, that the injector nozzle is open and fuel is being delivered to the manifold or injector body. The programming of the ECM that controls these functions, called "mapping," tailors operation to the needs of the power plant.

Let us put this system to the test and follow it through the start/run cycle.

When the switch key is turned on in an EFI system, the fuel pump begins to run. Fuel is supplied to the rail and thence to the injectors. The entire system is pressurized in an instant and ready to go.

The ECM already knows what the temperature is. There is no need for a conventional choke. At the first revolution, the ECM will cycle the injectors. This provides a shot of raw gas to the manifold and richens up the air/fuel supply for a cold start.

When the engine turns over and pressure drops in the cylinders, they will get a supply of fuel-laden air almost instantly. The engine starts quickly and the ECM immediately begins to react to numerous inputs.

The throttle position sensor tells the ECM if more speed is required. Other sensors are telling the ECM the temperature in the engine at all times. The ECM continuously adjusts the fuel flow, based on the information it is receiving.

The ECM also monitors spark timing and engine load, which we will cover later. It adjusts the fuel supply to allow for load conditions, altitude, possible detonation and other factors.

The fact that fuel is supplied to the injector under pressure is really only a part of the EFI story. That pressure delivers fuel through the pintle or nozzle at pressures varying from about 35 lbs./in.^{2} to 55 lbs./in.^{2}. The fuel is thoroughly atomized by this pressure.

The manifold must still have a pressure drop inside its ports or runners to deliver air to the cylinders. Yet there is no need for a venturi effect, so this flow speed can be adjusted accordingly. The EFI engine can flow large quantities of air down its manifold.

However, it cannot be allowed to lose so much flow speed that the atomized fuel tends to settle out or puddle in the port runners. As with the carbureted engine, flow speed still has an effect.

Performance tuning an EFI system is really quite simple if you have the computer, the codes and a bit of know-how. □It is not enough to know how to work the computer. You must also understand the effect of your actions upon the engine itself. □Every change affects the entire engine.

Mechanics often forget this. They sometimes do things to the engine that may be perfectly sound for one facet of operation but fail totally in the context of operation for the whole engine.

As with the carburetor, you should spend a bit of time with a competent practitioner on a flow bench if you really want to understand injectors.

We have now explored both carburetors and injectors as fuel delivery systems. But you may still wonder, "Which is better, the carburetor or the injector?" There is honestly not a definitive answer.

In general, the injector is more flexible and has a great deal going for it, but the carburetor is not a total loss. When it is operating within its optimum range, it is very efficient.

It is also very reliable. It is less expensive, is simple to service, inexpensive to repair and it will serve quite well for many purposes. Do not turn against the carburetor just yet. It will be with us for a while.

Contrary to popular belief, the injector does not make more power in the engine simply because it injects fuel. The injector is mapped electronically for performance or economy, and it cannot do both.

In fact, at full throttle, the EFI unit does not operate any more cheaply than does the carbureted engine. Both systems require about the same amount of fuel for full-power operation.

Gasoline fuels have two qualities, viscosity and abrasiveness.

Viscosity is flow friction or resistance to flow. It is measured by the amount of any liquid that passes through an orifice of known diameter in a given interval. This flow friction is responsible for the tendency of gasoline to create static electricity as it flows through a tube or hose, and it is the main reason we must ground our filler necks or fuel tanks to prevent an explosion.

Abrasiveness is the tendency to abrade or grind away at anything with which it comes into contact. Over the years, this abrasion affects jets or other parts of the carburetor.

It also affects injector nozzles. In the early years of EFI systems, the static electricity generated by this flow friction produced current flows that were a problem for the ECM.

CHAPTER SIX

INTAKE MANIFOLDS

Intake manifolds receive an air/fuel mix from the carburetor or air box and deliver it to the cylinder heads. This is a pretty straightforward operation, but there is a bit more happening than that. The air/fuel charge must be well mixed.

Of course, we want to deliver as much of this mixture as possible with as little loss as we can manage. First, let us consider the physical shape of an intake manifold and then move on to its operation.

The intake manifold itself is a funny-looking lump of cast iron or aluminum that sits atop or alongside the engine. It has a group of passages cast into its body and these are called port runners, which appear to emerge from a kind of box.

This box is the plenum chamber, and the carburetor or throttle body injection system bolts to the top of it on engines that are so equipped. The air intake for a tuned port injection system also bolts to the top of the intake manifold.

On the in-line engine, the intake manifold is usually bolted to the side of the cylinder head. On the V shaped engine configuration, the manifold sits in the valley, that area between the cylinder heads.

Here the manifold serves as a cover for the camshaft and cam followers. The intake manifold restrains oil sprayed around inside the engine. A leak at this joint could allow the intake to pull oil from the valley and burn it.

Both types of intake manifolds, for in-line or V blocked engines, are attached to the cylinder head with a group of bolts, and a machined surface mates the manifold to the cylinder head. A gasket seals the joint.

This is a special gasket that must react to the movement of the block and maintain its seal. Special care must be taken when installing this gasket because leakage is possible for oil, water, exhaust gasses and the air/fuel mix.

The intake manifold is a single casting and it does not have any individual parts. The thermostat housing is attached to the front of the intake manifold, however. Within this housing lies the thermostat itself, which reacts to coolant temperature and opens or closes as temperatures fluctuate. The thermostat keeps temperatures in the engine at an even level. Too cool is as great a problem as too hot.

The thermostat housing generally holds the temperature sending unit, which operates off electrical resistance. It measures resistance at the sender, provides the figures to the temperature gauge, and the temperature gauge reads out in degrees. With no actual parts to consider, shape and function come into play. First, let's look at an intake manifold in a carbureted system, then touch on the intake manifold in an EFI system. They are not the same.

Because the air/fuel mix moves first from the carburetor into the plenum chamber, we'll begin there.

We must have the plenum chamber because it receives that fresh, incoming charge from the carburetor. It also distributes the charge to the individual runners and is able to fool the sonic, which emerges from the cylinders.

Emerging from the plenum chamber are the spaghetti-shaped runners, which are the passages down which fuel travels to the engine. These runners are subject to the same physical laws as those that affect the carburetor.

If the flow velocity in these runners is high enough, the fuel will remain suspended in the air going down the runners and will be burned more efficiently. Slow the flow, and the fuel may puddle in the runners.

At the same time, this restriction is causing the loss of potential air/fuel mix to the engine. Sorry, the compromise is necessary. It is also costly in terms of engine performance. We are losing flow.

There are no ready answers for this problem, and that is only one of the limitations imposed by manifolds and manifold runners. If you look closely at the manifold, you will see that the runners are not the same length.

On the V-6 or V-8 engine there is one runner for every two cylinders. The foremost and rearmost cylinders are farther away from the carburetor than the center cylinders. Thus they are further from the air/fuel supply.

This means the fresh air/fuel charge has farther to go, down a longer runner, to reach these more remote cylinders. The flow velocity will become somewhat slower and the tendency for the fuel to puddle will be somewhat greater for the end cylinders.

The in-line engine has an even greater problem. Consider the straight 6 and its log-type intake manifold, which runs the length of the engine. The end cylinders on this manifold are a real problem.

Because these end cylinders are remote from the manifold centerline, the distance alone leads to starvation and puddling. □This manifold has other problems, as well.

The individual runners from the log to the cylinders are set at right angles to the manifold. The sharp turn in the flow of the air/fuel mix not only restricts the flow but also causes turbulence in the runners.

The most efficient approach, of course, would be equal-length and equal-diameter runners.

Port runners of equal length and with equal diameters should charge the cylinders equally. This would be a boon to the engine.

Unfortunately, this is an expensive alternative. Although custom manifolds are available with equal-length port runners, they are all configured for the very maximum performance and are useless to the ordinary boater.

Another problem for the standard intake manifold is the direction change. Those tortuous turns and twists in the runners cause restrictions in the flow of the air/fuel mix and tend to cause puddling.

Every turn in that runner impedes and reduces the flow of the new charge to the cylinder. At every turn, the incoming flow is slower on the inside of the bend. The chance of the fuel puddling out of the air stream increases in that slower-moving air mass.

Again, that custom manifold can minimize or even eradicate the problem, but it's costly. □The manifold runner on the standard intake manifold is, like the venturi on the carburetor, a compromise.

There also are two other passages in the intake manifold.

One is across the front section of the manifold and it transfers coolant from one side of the block to the other. This balances the cooling effects so that the sides of the engine maintains a common temperature.

The other passage is just beneath the plenum chamber. It runs from exhaust manifold to exhaust manifold, side to side. The hot gasses are intended to heat the air/fuel mix as the engine warms up.

This passage was originally designed for the automobile and was intended to become inactive after the engine warmed up. On the marine engine. this passage is usually blocked off. Its purpose is not appropriate to marine use.

The gasket set that serves the intake manifold has a set of interlocking plates that block this passage, and you must be aware of this need when you overhaul the engine. At the bottom of the intake manifold below the plenum, there may be a heat shield.

This is made of sheet metal and isolates the hot spot in

the manifold from the crankcase oil that is thrown against the underside of the manifold by lifters and the camshaft.

This heat would burn or char the oil and cause deterioration.

What about intake manifolds for the tuned port injection? This unit is a bit different in design. The injector is threaded into the port itself, very near the cylinder head. As with the carbureted manifold, the runners are not the same length.

The injector delivers fuel to the same part of the manifold runner for each cylinder, however, and the fuel-laden air has the same short distance to travel for all cylinders.

Thus, the fuel is introduced into the air stream, well atomized, at a point equidistant from every cylinder.

The TPI manifold can flow more air for several reasons. It can more easily be tuned for ram effect and it can use the sonic -- a problem for the carbureted engine -- to its benefit.

Let's take a look at the sonic, first talking about tuning, not as it applies to tune-ups but as it applies to sound waves and their effects upon engine performance.

When the air/fuel mix is burned inside the cylinder, it creates a sound wave called a pulse or sonic. This sound wave can create pressure, and the pressure wave is said to have a value.

On the intake side of the engine, the sonic develops a wave that comes up the port runners from the cylinders with a negative value. This means the sonic wave is actually trying to pull that incoming air/fuel charge down into the engine.

The rule says, "If the sonic does not hit anything, it will return, back down the port runner, driving before it a wave with the opposite value than that it carried up the pipe." Now the sonic is trying to push the incoming air/fuel mix toward the cylinder.

Both these activities can be useful, but they can also be a problem. This effect has a time element and it only works to our benefit if that wave is working in phase with the valve timing. If the sonic is out of time, it will hurt rather than help.

In a carbureted system, the sonic can destroy engine performance by interrupting the flow of air down the carburetor throat if it resonates out of phase, or is not properly timed. The timing of this wave is controlled by the length of the port runner.

Unfortunately, this effect only works through a narrow band of rpms. The engine must be tuned for a given rpm band or the speed at which the sonic resonates in phase. Within this narrow band of rpms, the sonic enhances engine performance.

Outside this rpm band, the sonic is disruptive. In a carbureted system, for the stock engine, we must forgo the high-speed benefits to negate the low-speed losses. This is what the plenum chamber does for us. It fools the sonic, which collapses in the chamber.

We have lost the benefits but saved ourselves from the losses. The engine works well through a broad band of Rpms, unaffected by the sonic. The engine simply goes on it's merry way and we contain the sonic in the plenum.

The electronic fuel injector has a different potential because it delivers its fuel under pressure. With the EFI, we can afford to use the sonic because fuel will be delivered to the port runners, very near the cylinder, regardless of some fluctuation in pulses from the sonic.

Thus, with the EFI system, we are able to take advantage of this pulsing, deriving considerable benefit at times and feeling little loss at others. I am going to pursue this matter in depth in the chapter on Induction Systems.

How about those custom intake manifolds? There are as many available as the waves in the sea and almost as many manufacturers. □There are some truly wonderful creations on the market, and if I were to offer one word of advice in their selection it would be "balance."

Some of those custom manifolds do not have a plenum chamber. They are designed with long port runners and are intended to operate at very high speed only, giving efficient performance through a very narrow rpm band. Before you buy a custom manifold, be sure you know what you are doing.

When we bring all of the parts of the induction system together, you will see the significance of balanced flows on both sides of the engine. But for now, keep in mind: The carburetor flow characteristics must balance with those of the intake manifold itself.

The use of a high-performance or high-efficiency after-market intake manifold can provide a significant advantage but its use assumes a balance between carburetor and manifold. Unbalanced parts in the engine will guarantee an uneasy union.

A higher CFM carburetor on a stock manifold may not flow as much air/fuel mix as the stocker did. In time you will begin to realize that all the parts of the induction system are truly dependent upon one another.

CHAPTER SEVEN

CAMSHAFTS

The camshaft, like the intake manifold, is a single casting, but probably no part of an engine has enjoyed more notoriety. □In Chapter One, we described the camshaft and how it works.

Now let's expand on its design and operation.

The camshaft has one lobe for each valve. The lobe design is a pretty exotic piece of work, and that design is crucial to engine performance.

There are four principle measurements of camshafts. The first is lift, which can be defined as the distance the cam follower will rise or fall during one complete rotation of the camshaft.

This is referred to as gross lift, as opposed to net lift. Leave net lift alone for now and think about gross lift in a second way. Gross lift is also the distance a valve would rise or fall in a single revolution if the camshaft were working directly against the valve stem, with no clearance.

The second important aspect of camshaft measurement is duration, or the amount of time, expressed in degrees of crankshaft rotation, when the valve will remain open. Duration is measured at several positions of the camshaft by many custom tuners for various reasons.

The third measurement is overlap, which is the time,

measured in crankshaft degrees, when the intake and exhaust valves will be open simultaneously. This situation is necessary but can be a problem.

The fourth measure is the distance between the lobe centers, which affects flow characteristics of the engine. We shuffle the lobe centers dramatically for many of our special-application engines.

Let us look at an individual lobe. The lobe itself dictates the amount of lift and the number of degrees of duration. The exact shape of the lobe is called a profile, which decides what the individual lobe will accomplish.

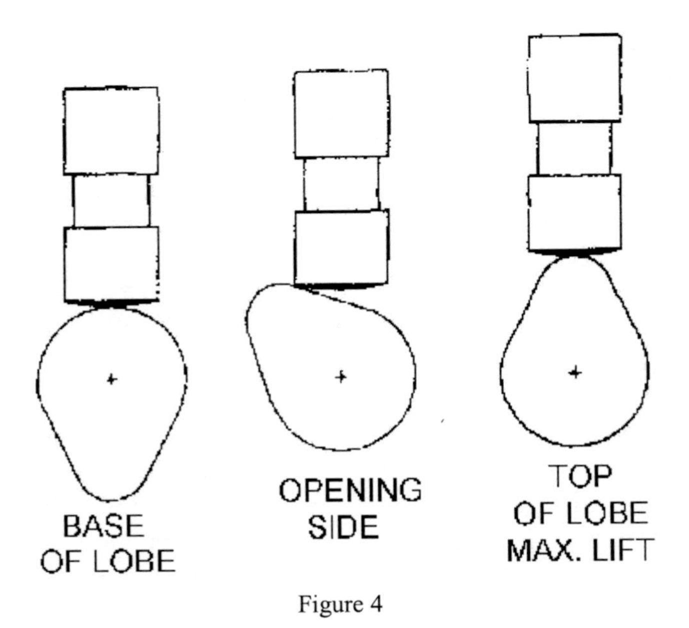

Figure 4

Operation of the cam lobe.

Consider a single lobe and let us see how a profile is developed for it. First establish a center for the camshaft itself. Now draw a vertical line through that center and we have established a center line for the lobe. Now comes the great circle.

Select a radius for the great circle. The great circle will be the bottom radius of the lobe, but we will draw it as a complete circle of 360 degrees. Now select the amount of total lift you want to achieve. Move to the top center position on the outside perimeter of the great circle.

Along your established center line, measure off a distance equal to the amount of lift you want in the camshaft. Add this measurement to the outside radius of the great circle. You now have the total height for the top of the lobe.

Go back to the bottom of the lobe and begin to follow the great circle. When you have reached the point on the camshaft rotation where lift is desired, you will begin to increase the radius of the great circle. When that radius increases, you will no longer have a circle.

The exact point of this increase changes the circle to an eccentric or lobe and lift begins here. The lift must be gradual enough to allow the cam follower (lifter) to remain in contact with the camshaft. If the lift is too rapid, the follower may bounce, and one or both will fail.

On the other side of the camshaft you will reduce the lift back to zero, gradually returning the lobe profile to the radius of the great circle and ending the lift cycle. The shape of the profile must allow for one further consideration.

How fast the valve will open/close is dictated by the ramps incorporated into its construction. The camshaft lobe incorporates a series of these ramps, such as an opening ramp or an acceleration ramp, that are involved in the operation of the valve.

The opening ramp initially begins to lift the follower, while the acceleration ramp speeds up this motion. The shape of these ramps must consider both what is needed and what is possible. The needs of the engine are important.

The engine will demand a different amount of air/fuel mix for each degree of crankshaft rotation. The size of the valves, the amount of flow at any given time, the size of the port runners, the type and size of the carburetor, all help to decide how much can be delivered.

The camshaft profile must attempt to satisfy all these considerations for good performance.

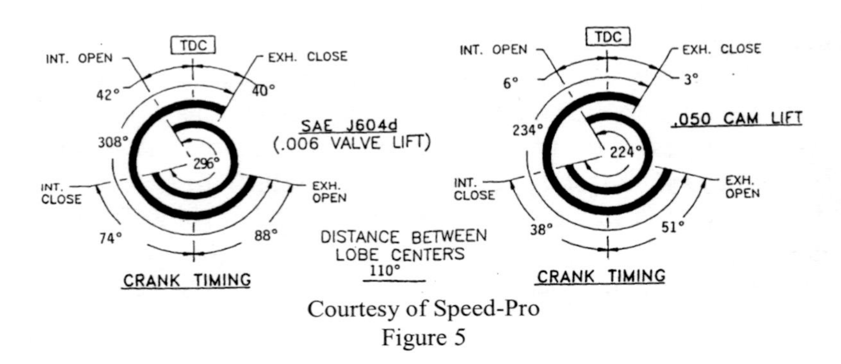

Courtesy of Speed-Pro
Figure 5

Typical camshaft specification.

Yet, what is ideal for performance is limited by the ability of the cam follower to follow that lobe at all times. This situation limits what we can ultimately do with the engine itself.

The number of mathematical calculations that go into the design of a camshaft lobe is staggering. We once had to make these calculations by hand, grind an entire camshaft and try it out.

Now the computer does this for us and saves us a great deal of time. The Computer Assisted Design (CAD) unit can create an entire engine or any part thereof.

It can then run that engine with our new camshaft design aboard. You can change any aspect of the camshaft you wish at any time, and the CAD unit will adjust.

We have disposed of lift and duration. The camshaft designer will tell you anything you want to know about these two numbers, but few are willing to discuss profiles or lobe design beyond this point.

Overlap and lobe center spacings are controlled by the profile of the lobes and by the position of the individual lobes on the camshaft. The overlap is a product of these two components, duration and lobe center spacing.

The camshaft profile will dictate when lift begins and how long it continues. The position of the lobe centers will decide the times when these two activities are affecting both valves at the same moment.

Overlap is crucial to the operation of the engine, but if it is excessive, it can lead to disaster. Let us begin with the beneficial effects of overlap and then move on to its less-desirable attributes.

Overlap allows for the use of inertia in the charging of the cylinder. Assume that both valves are open and the engine is ready to begin the intake stroke. The rapid flow of gasses is already established. Exhaust gasses are still pouring out of the engine on one side, while a fresh charge from the intake manifold is entering the cylinder.

Inertia causes both flows to continue in the proper direction, so long as we have the speed and strength of flow to make this happen. Intake gasses are helping the exhaust gasses out, while exhaust gasses are helping the incoming charge to fill the cylinder.

Consider a different scenario. The piston is going down on the intake stroke, both intake and exhaust valves are open. Again, we are trying to charge the cylinder, but we are at idle speed and many things are different.

Port flow velocities are fairly slow and the air/fuel mix is moving at a lazy pace down the port runners. With both valves open, the engine may pull from the exhaust side also. This effect is called reversion. The greater the overlap, the more the reversionary effect.

We seldom have a problem with this in stock engines because the overlap is small and the reversion effect is minimal. On high-performance engines with extended overlap periods, we may pull water from the exhaust manifold back into the engine on the reversion cycle.

That can be destructive and it happens more often than you think. Before you decide to buy a high-performance camshaft, make some allowance in your exhaust system for this reversionary effect. Your mechanic can help.

Would you like to really see how this all works?

Take a camshaft and set it up on centers. Affix a degree wheel and, on one of the lobes, position a dial indicator. You can slowly rotate the camshaft and plainly see what is going on.

As the camshaft rotates, the dial will follow the bottom of the lobe without changing dimension. You are following the arc of the great circle. At some point in this rotation, the dial will begin to move. This is the beginning of lift in the camshaft.

The point on the degree wheel at which lift first occurs is the point where the valve will open, if there is no lash or clearance in the valve adjustment. I have turned a system like this for hours, observing the valve open, valve closed and other figures. Fascinating.

Always remember that we are operating a four-cycle engine and that any figures taken from the camshaft rather than the crankshaft are at half value. The camshaft is running at half the speed of the crankshaft and the events that occur are also at half speed.

Lift figures are given in actual measurements taken from the camshaft, but figures involving rotation are given in crankshaft degrees.

We are going to move from here to the section on valve trains and you will see how these two are further related.

CHAPTER EIGHT

VALVE TRAIN

The valve train consists of the cam followers, push rods, rocker arms, valves themselves and valve springs. Let us approach each of these parts.

The cam follower is commonly called a lifter or tappet and it may be solid or hydraulic. The solid lifter is about ¾ inch in diameter and about 2 1/2 inches high, although these dimensions vary from engine to engine.

It has a flat bottom and a machined socket on top to accept the push rod. The hydraulic cam follower has a cushioned, oil-filled body with a piston inside that rides on a cushion of oil. A socket is machined into the piston for the push rod.

Some high-performance engines and the latest, stock marine engines use a roller tappet. This is a cam follower with a wheel on the bottom that rolls across the cam lobe instead of dragging across it. The roller tappet reduces friction and saves horsepower. It does not wear the camshaft as rapidly and it can follow more radical profiles without floating away.

The roller tappet can be solid or hydraulic. High-rpm camshafts -- shafts designed to turn more than 6,500 rpms -- usually have solid lifters.

The cam follower rides in machined webbings called lifter holes located just above the camshaft in the cylinder block. The oil gallery has oil delivery passages drilled into the lifter holes. Oil for the cam followers is delivered here.

The push rod is a hollow piece of metal tubing about 8 inches long that sits atop the cam follower and fits into a socket in the rocker arm. This is a very stiff piece of metal with a hardened ball joint on each end to work inside those sockets.

Oil to lubricate the rocker arms and the valve stems is carried from the cam followers to the rocker arms through the push rods. A great deal of pressure is exerted on the push rod, which must be light as well as stiff.

The rocker arm looks like an oblong cup. It is usually stamped from sheet metal about 0.125-inch thick and has a socket at each end. The push rod rides in one end and the valve stem in the other. There is a ball socket joint in the approximate middle of this rocker arm.

The rocker arm may have a 1:1 ratio. This means the arm is the same length on both sides of the ball joint. It may also have an unbalanced length with ratios, usually of 1:1.5 or 1:1.7.

Figure 6

High performance rocker arm assembly.

The rocker arm sits atop a rocker stud, which is a bolt or pin screwed or pressed into the proper bosses in the cylinder head. This stud holds the ball joint and adjustment screw that the rocker arm rides in.

The rocker arm may be a roller rocker. □This refers to the ball joint at the middle of the arm and to the friction point at the end of the arm that contacts the valve stem. Roller bearings at either of these contact points reduce friction and add usable horsepower to the engine.

A surprising number of the newer vortec engines, as well as others, use both the roller rockers and the roller lifters. The gain for a full roller valve train can be as much as 15 horsepower. For high-performance engines, it can be even more.

The valves are riding in a guide, which is a machined area running from just inside the cylinder head to the top of the cylinder head. These guides serve as bearings for the movement of the valves.

The valves are supported by their stems, which protrude from inside the ports to the top of the cylinder head. They are encircled by the valve springs. There may be one to three springs per valve.

The springs are held in place by a retainer, which is a disc-shaped piece of metal that is held in place with a set of valve locks. Valve locks are two pear-shaped pieces of metal that fit into slots in the valve stems.

A valve stem seal on the intake valves prevent oil from being drawn down the guide and into the intake ports and burned. These seals may be as simple as a kind of rubber ring, not unlike a square-sided O-ring. They may be more elaborate.

Now let's see how the parts of the valve train work. We begin at the camshaft. The camshaft rotates and the lobe begins to lift the follower. As the follower rises, it imparts an upward motion to the push rod.

Hey. Wrong way. The valve wants to move downward. That is why we need the rocker arm, to change the direction of this force generated by the camshaft. The push rod pushes one side of the rocker arm upward and the other side of the rocker arm pushes the valve downward.

As previously noted, the rocker arms may not be direct acting units. A direct acting rocker has a 1:1 ratio. The 1:1 rocker arm moves the valve the same distance the camshaft moves the rocker arm.

There are rocker arms in fairly common use with ratios of 1.5:1 and 1.7:1. With these rocker arms, the short side is toward the push rod, while the long side is toward the valve. The lift in the camshaft is multiplied at the valve. Here is an example:

A camshaft with a lift figure of .287, using a rocker arm with a 1:1.7 ratio would have a gross lift of 0.4879 or about .480. The lift is multiplied by the ratio in the arm. Of course, this creates a secondary problem: The valve spring pressure is increased also.

The load on the cam lobe is increase by a multiple of 1.7:1. Everything is a tradeoff at some point. □We can use a multiplying rocker arm to give more lift to the valve, but we will increase the wear on the camshaft.

The valve is moving against pressure from the valve spring. The valve spring has two figures we often measure. The on-seat pressure is the proper pressure for the spring to maintain while the valve is at rest upon its seat. The valve-open pressure is the pressure the spring exerts upon the valve at full lift. Both should be within specifications provided by the manufacturer or the springs will need attention.

The springs have a vibration length, and when vibrations in the engine reach a certain frequency, they may collapse. This problem may be solved by multiple springs. They are wound to different specifications and they collapse at different frequencies.

The larger spring may collapse early on and recover as the rpms vary and frequencies change. The smaller spring will collapse at higher rpms and, it too, will recover as the frequencies change. When the engine reaches max rpms, both springs have recovered.

The third spring, if one is present, is a vibration damper. Many engines still use a single spring, some use two and some employ all three. It depends upon the camshaft design and the designer's preference.

As the camshaft continues to rotate, the cam follower will reach the top of the lobe. This is maximum lift and, after this point, the follower begins its trip down the back side of the lobe. The valve begins to close.

In another chapter, we will discuss Induction Systems, or the exhaust process. □The exhaust process is actually a part of the intake process, and vice versa. This integrated flow across a well-designed engine is harmonious. If the flows do not balance, we have a kind of chaos and the engine does not fare well.

CHAPTER NINE

CYLINDER HEAD

The cylinder head supports the rocker arms, rocker studs, valves and their springs. It is a heavy casting, usually made of iron but occasionally of aluminum. It has passages called ports that deliver gasses to and from the engine.

Other passages carry coolant around the inside of the head to cool the head, combustion chamber, valve seats, etc. The head also has drain down holes that allow lubricating oil to drain from the rockers and valves back to the crankcase.

The combustion chamber may be cast or machined into the cylinder head and it is here that the air/fuel mix begins to burn. The combustion chamber appears to the uninitiated as simply a big hole in the cylinder head, but it actually has a very sophisticated design.

The valve seats are machined into this combustion chamber. The seats may be machined into the head itself and those can be hardened or left as manufactured.

Other seats may be made separately of hard metal and inserted. These seats are usually made of stellite or a similar metal that resists heat and the constant pounding of the valve itself. □They are called hard seats or inserted seats and, while they are not cheap, they are highly desirable.

The combustion chamber is the roof of the cylinder and its size controls the compression ratio. That ratio can be calculated by comparing the volume of the cylinder displacement with that of the combustion chamber.

Combustion chamber volumes are usually given in cubic centimeters (cc), but to make a comparison we must convert to cubic inches. Let us assume a combustion chamber volume of 10 cubic inches and a cylinder volume of 100 cubic inches.

Now, according to the rule for ratio and proportion, substitute in the formula,

100 : 10 : x : 1. We see here that 10x = 100 and x = 10. Substitute the 10 for x and we get a 10:1 compression ratio. This is called a theoretical compression ratio.

This is the figure generally given with any engine and it is not exactly accurate. If you want the exact numbers, you must know what the camshaft timing is. The engine does not make compression until the last valve closes.

Your first volume, the one based upon the cubic displacement of the engine, would not be valid. For that first volume, the figure "V1," you would need to calculate the volume of the cylinder at the moment when the last valve closed. You could then proceed as before.

The final number, the actual compression ratio, would be less than the number for the theoretical compression ratio. This is not a practiced deception, but it does mean that a single engine may be sold with more than one type of camshaft installed.

The chamber is made in several shapes and each has a name.

There are hemispherical chambers and pent roof chambers on some engines. The most common combustion chamber shape for a marine engine today is the wedge.

Although the hemispherical chamber and the pent roof chamber have some advantages, let's stick with the common wedge chamber for our discussion.

The cylinder head must be rigid. It holds a seal against the deck or top of the cylinder block, aided by a cylinder head gasket. This seal must be complete while gasket and joint are assailed by hundreds of pounds of pressure and high temperatures. □

The cylinder head grows and shrinks as it is heated and cooled. This movement is common to both the overall dimensions and to localized areas where higher temperatures are present. Thus, the cylinder head is constantly flexing, yet we expect this gasket to hold and to seal.

There are a few aluminum cylinder heads out there, but most are made of cast iron. The aluminum heads are usually on aluminum engines.

Years ago, a few aluminum heads were placed on cast iron blocks. These cylinder heads were generally on high-performance applications, where aluminum heads offer several advantages. They handle heat well, reduce weight and transfer heat to the coolant rapidly. Yet they have one terrible problem.

The coefficient of expansion, the amount of growth caused by a given temperature, is the same for like metals. A cast-iron block and a cast-iron head should grow or shrink at approximately the same rate for the same number of degrees of temperature change.

The aluminum head, however, grows and shrinks at a different rate and trying to keep a head gasket sealed against two castings that move at a different rate in response to temperature is difficult.

Intake and exhaust passages that run through the heads are never shaped exactly as we would desire. We have never found a way to get the valves into the head without having them run through the port runners. This necessitates a bowl that is cast into the port.

The bowl is like a junction and gasses flow through it, while the valve guide and valve stem are restrictions extending into it. These restrictions also cause turbulence within it.

The water passages in the head, the allowance for cylinder head bolts, all of these things demand their own space. This situation makes for a great deal of compromise.

Spark plugs protrude into the combustion chamber through the cylinder head. They are threaded into the head and they may enter the combustion chamber, either straight in or at an angle. The heads are designated as straight plug heads or angle plug heads.

The angle plug head is by far the most common. The plugs in an angle plug head do not necessarily enter in the same direction. The angle of entry is the same, but each plug faces the flow direction of the gasses coming into the combustion chamber. This situation varies from engine to engine.

The size of the spark plug also varies. The 10 millimeter (mm) and 14 mm spark plugs are the only sizes in common use today.

Rocker studs that support the rocker arms may be pressed or screwed into the cylinder head. Those that are pressed in are by far the more common. The pressed-in rocker stud does fine for normal use, but should never be used with any high-performance parts.

A camshaft with higher lift or a valve spring with greater pressure may jack the studs right out of the block and the result can be disastrous. Even factory-built, high-performance engines will have screwed-in rocker studs.

The cylinder heads may be fitted with guide plates, which are small plates retained by the screwed in rocker studs. and which have two slots cut into their sides. The push rods ride in two slots cut into the sides of the guide plates, and the plates keep the push rods from walking about.

The side-to-side movement we call walking is usually not a problem until engine rpms exceed 4,500, but many marine engines can run at 5,000 rpms or more.

The cylinder heads are major castings and they rank second only to the cylinder block itself in importance. They support many important parts and fulfill many important functions.

CHAPTER TEN

EXHAUST MANIFOLDS

Exhaust manifolds are clumsy-looking at best and downright ugly at their worst. But I do love 'em. That stupid-looking chunk of metal can produce terrible back pressures and rob the engine of substantial amounts of power, but it does have another face to show.

A properly designed exhaust system can produce many added horsepower for the engine, sometimes as much as 20 percent. But that is further down the road. □Right now, let us begin with a simple lump of cast iron or aluminum.

Into this hunk of metal, we have cast passages intended for the discharge of burned gasses. Add a water jacket cast around these passages for the distribution of coolant and you have the simplest form of exhaust manifold.

Stock manifolds are generally the log type or the center-riser. The log type has been with us forever, but the center riser is a more recent system.

The older, log-type manifold ran the full length of the engine. The exhaust elbow was at the extreme end of the manifold and each successive cylinder was battling the next for access to that elbow.

The center riser manifold has the elbow in the middle. Cylinders exhaust upward, in a natural direction.

Hot gasses naturally tend to rise, so that upswept pipe

flows the gasses more easily and exerts less back pressure upon the cylinders. Center-riser manifolds employ an individual passage for each cylinder, up to the point where the common discharge enters the elbow.

For this reason the cylinders do not interfere with one another. Any pulses in the pipe are retained within that particular cylinder and do not become a problem for an adjacent cylinder.

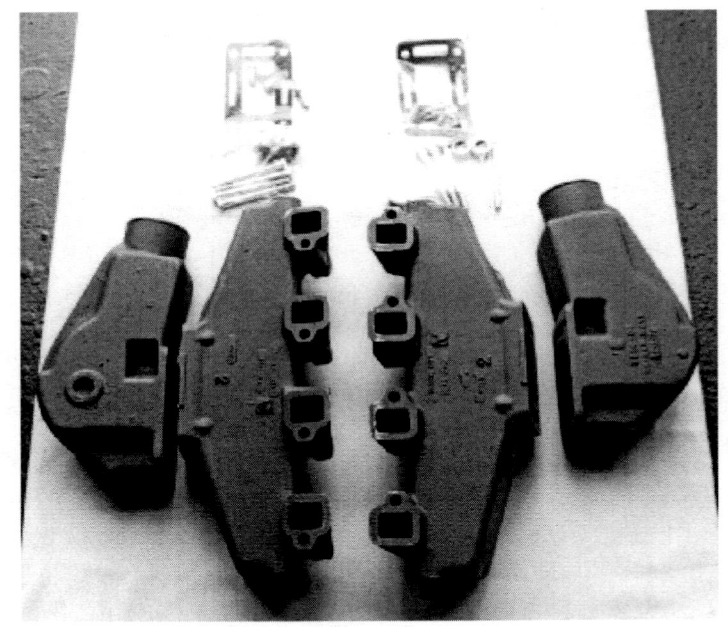

Figure 8

Exhaust manifold and riser assembly.

More exotic exhaust systems are made of tubing. They are called extractor exhausts because they actively help remove those burned exhaust gasses.

Remember that sonic wave we described in the chapter on intake manifolds? That same sonic also works on the exhaust side of the engine, except that it works in reverse. The exhaust valve opens and the sonic exits down the pipe with a positive value, pushing the exhaust gasses ahead of it.

If the sonic hits no obstruction, it will return up the pipe with a negative value, pulling those gasses out of the pipe. Thus, this system is referred to as an extractor exhaust.

Of course, this effect has some limits. The sonic effect must be timed and it only works through a narrow band of rpms. When that pipe resonates in phase, the effect can be awesome. When it resonates out of phase, it can be a real problem.

Stock engines are generally built to work without the sonic on both sides of the engine. High-performance engines generally take full advantage of this phenomenon.

That pipey effect is acceptable, and the poor low-end performance is acceptable to get that tremendous boost on the top end. Again, the classic tradeoff.

Naturally we wonder why an exhaust manifold for the stock engine needs to be so heavy and so ungainly. Exhaust manifolds are subjected to terrible vibrations from the sonic and from the engine block. They must be strong and they must be stiff. The bolts that hold them are high-tensile parts. Both the manifold and the bolts must resist the attack of saltwater.

The saltwater threat combines with temperatures approaching 1,000 degrees in the exhaust passages.

The port runners that carry those gasses from the heads to the manifold are exposed to the air. These runners and the flanges that bolt the manifold to the cylinder head are going to rust. In time, they will fail. In fact, the entire manifold is operating in a constant state of deterioration. This is the reason for its heavy construction.

The more metal it has in the walls and passages, the longer it will take for those passages to rust through.

How about stainless-steel exhausts? If they were cast and made of heavy construction, I think that they would do well. Unfortunately, those thin, welded jobs made of sheet metal do not seem to handle vibration well.

How about the exhaust elbow? That is a casting that also seems to require weight and heft to last.

The elbow makes the direction change from vertical discharge to horizontal discharge. The water passages in the elbow are heavy -- just as they are in the exhaust manifold -- to resist corrosion. Vibration is a problem for the elbow also, just as it is for the manifold.

The mating surface where elbow meets manifold is machined to accurate dimensions. This joint is one of the most important connections on your engine. If you see rust at this point, disassemble the unit and inspect it carefully.

Any leakage through this joint will send coolant, generally sea water, into the engine and will wreck the valves and possibly the pistons. Buy only factory gaskets for this joint and never use any sealant on this gasket.

Remove the elbows at least annually or at the first sign of leakage and check for a proper seal. The walls of the elbow and the walls of the exhaust manifold should be at least 1/4 inch thick around this joint. If either is thinner, replace the part.

Both the manifold and the elbow for use on the stock engine should have passages of the largest diameter available. These passages are water-filled from the elbow rearward, and this causes a back pressure on the cylinder of the engine.

This back pressure tends to interrupt the flow of exhaust gasses and, thus, it is an impediment to engine operation. The larger elbows are better able to handle the flows and offer less restriction.

The elbow can be spaced away from the manifold with a spacer or riser. These fittings usually come in 2-inch increments and they raise the level of the exhaust discharge higher in the bilges. These risers are designed to prevent water from entering the engine.

Reverse flows tend to come back up the exhaust hose from the outside water if the angle between elbow and discharge hose is not great enough. If you are having trouble with water incursion or that reversionary cycle that we mentioned before, try a riser.

The elbow discharges cooling water into the exhaust hose. The tip of the elbow has a diffuser in the discharge area. This diffuser distributes cooling water equally around the perimeter of the exhaust hose to prevent hot spots.

The diffuser is a kind of restriction that can get stopped up. Rust, salt buildup and other elements tend to block this discharge point. You must keep the diffuser clear, because blockage at this point can cause the engine to overheat on one side of the block and destroy one manifold. Of course, if both sides are blocked, it can wipe the engine out entirely.

There are exhaust manifolds with single bolt holes on the mounting flanges that attach the manifold to the head. There are also manifolds with double bolt holes on the flanges. I prefer the double flange because this is an area subject to severe deterioration.

No manifolds have too much meat in those flanges. Get the manifold with the thickest flanges you can find. □They will rust out soon enough and there is little else you can do about it.

We have the individual parts of the induction system at hand. Now let us put them all into motion at the same time.

CHAPTER ELEVEN

INDUCTION SYSTEMS

You have been through the individual parts of the induction system and have seen how each part works. Now it is time to put them all together and see how they work as a team. The successful operation of the engine depends upon this teamwork.

We begin with the carburetor. Let us assume that we have a carburetor with a proper capacity for our engine. The manifold has port runners that match the carburetor, and it maintains flow velocities compatible with the needs of the carburetor. □The design and shape of the port runners in the manifold gives good flow characteristics and the intake ports in the cylinder head are well laid out. The valves are of a proper size and the camshaft has lift and overlap to match the rest of the system. The exhaust manifold is working well, the exhaust flow balances with the intake side of the engine and flow across the entire induction system is working smoothly. This is an engine in harmony with itself, and it should run very well.

How about that balanced flow we are hearing so much about? Let me offer you an illustration. □

On some of the engines that I have worked with we established flow velocities at about 285 feet per minute on the intake side of the engine and about 325 feet per minute on the exhaust side.

At this speed of flow, the intake manifold had a good ram effect and the exhaust manifold maintained good extraction, with the burned gasses leaving the cylinder very clear. How do these uneven numbers achieve an even flow?

There is a substantial difference in the amount of gas being flowed on the opposite sides of the engine. Expansion of the burning gasses, during combustion makes this difference in the volumes. This expanding gas makes the engine run.

The exhaust manifold must have larger passages than does the intake manifold, yet the flow will be faster through those larger passages. The flows complement each other because they each serve the needs of the engine.

Desirable flow velocities will vary with the rpms at which the engine is expected to provide optimum performance.

You may have some questions about valve sizes. The exhaust valve is always smaller than the intake valve, even though more gas is leaving the exhaust side.

Why? There are two reasons. First, the exhaust gas has a great deal of natural pressure to drive it out through the system. And, second, that higher flow velocity on the exhaust side establishes the inertia effect.

Let me give you an example. The Chevrolet small-block engine offers intake valves with diameters of 1.98 inches and 2.02 inches. At any rpm below 6,000, the 1.98 inch diameter valve will flow more gas than the larger 2.02 valve.

This assumes a ported cylinder head, a performance camshaft and an extractor exhaust; all of the little niceties that smooth and enhance flow characteristics. It also applies only at higher rpms in that 6,000 range.

Yet the performance is there and it proves three things conclusively: Bigger is not always better, flow velocity is a crucial consideration and inertia generated by that rapid flow does a lot to pack the cylinder.

You should be aware of altered operation, which

occurs every time there is a speed change. Suppose the operator decides to slow. The throttle is closed and the manifold pressure drops dramatically.

This happens because the engine has not quit turning at high rpms. Remember, the change cannot come instantly, and demand from the engine is still high. As the throttle butterfly closes off flow to the carburetor, the manifold pressure must fall.

Now the flow is out of balance and the mixture is very lean. The engine is losing speed. What happens when the emergency ends and the operator opens the throttle? Suddenly, the manifold pressure reverses itself. The engine rpms are down, and demand is down as well.

With the throttle open, pressure in the manifold rises rapidly, the flow slows down and the engine leans out. □This is why we have an accelerator pump. □When the throttle is opened again, the reduced flow in the system will not pull the needed fuel from the carburetor to feed the engine.

There are several things to be learned here. First, speed changes in the engine are always a problem. Second, they are costly. That shot of raw gas that we feed the engine on acceleration is necessary to keep the engine from staggering before it accelerates.

And because it provides more fuel than the engine uses, it is wasteful. □Keep your speed changes gradual and the engine will give better performance. It also will last longer. Rapid acceleration and deceleration can cause excessive wear in the engine.

The engine equipped with electronic fuel injection is largely immune to this problem. The ECM reacts to several sensory inputs. It knows the temperature of the engine, whether the mixture is rich or lean, and the pressure in the manifold, and it can react accordingly.

The ECM monitors engine condition continuously, enabling the injectors to furnish the proper amount of fuel to the engine at all times, regardless of fluctuating manifold pressures. There is no need for the accelerator pump, no need to overbalance the system at any time.

In the chapter on EFI systems, we noted that control is the forte of the EFI. □These systems give the technician complete control of the air/fuel/spark trio.

TROUBLE SHOOTING

We have talked about how the engine works. Now, what do I do if it does not work? There are initial checks to make on any engine.

Let's start with an engine that has quit suddenly.

Remember, to run, the engine must have air, fuel and spark, at the proper time. □First, check the fuel, voltage and temperature gauges. □Does the engine have fuel? Is current available? Is the engine overheated?

Are gauges OK? Remove the flash arrestor and have someone push the throttle forward and back two or three times. Watch the carburetor throats and see if gasoline is pumped into the throat. □There should be a visible stream.

No visible flow? You are not getting gasoline. Begin at the carburetor, working backward, until you find fuel: fuel pump, fuel filter, fuel lines, tank pickup, working the system back from the engine towards the tank.

What if you have fuel showing at the carburetor throat? What if you have a good flow of fuel off the accelerator pump?

Put the flash arrestor back into place and pull a lead off one of the spark plugs. I keep a spare plug aboard so I will not have to take one out of the engine. I put that spare plug in the spark plug lead and ground the plug on the engine. Forget about the paint.

If it has a proper spark, it will not matter. Get your helper to turn the engine over. A good spark will be blue/white and you will literally hear it crack.

If it is not there, take the high tension lead out of the coil. Hold it a half-inch from the cylinder head and turn the engine over again. If you have a good spark, the trouble may be in your distributor. The spark from the coil is going into the distributor but not coming out.

No spark at the coil? As with the fuel, begin tracking backward. The trouble is at the last place where you find a spark. Always track fuel, water and electrical problems backward from the end.

If you have fuel and spark but the engine still fails to start, you probably cannot do anything about this situation on the water. The loss of air flow comes from leaking valves, a broken timing chain or other internal problems, all outside the scope of on-water repairs.

If you take the engine to a shop or work on it ashore, begin with a compression check. This may seem wasteful if there is some small thing wrong that can be fixed immediately.

Yet, you cannot tune an engine with poor compression. In addition, we learn so much about the engine at this time. Pull the spark plugs out of all cylinders at once. Lay them out as they come from the engine. Now read the plugs before you start the compression check.

If you are not familiar with this procedure, get a chart from any spark plug manufacturer that shows the many colors you may encounter on the individual insulators and explains what each indicates.

Run your compression check with the throttle wide open. Keep the figures from each cylinder numbered to match the spark plug from that cylinder. Now you can use the plug readings to reinforce your findings from the compression check.

A good mechanic can tell you if the engine is running too hot or too cold, if the spark plugs have the proper heat range, if the engine is running lean or rich, if the carburetor is functioning properly, if the engine is burning oil and an unbelievable number of things from the combination of plug readings and compression pressures.

The service manual will tell you what the compression readings should be at any given cylinder. The minimum reading should not be down by more than 15 $lbs./in.^2$ The balance from the lowest to the highest cylinder should not vary by more than that figure.

For example, if the factory calls for compression pressures at 130 to 135 $lbs./in.^2$, your reading should not be less than 115 psi and no cylinder should vary by more than 15 psi from the lowest to the highest.

What do we do about EFI engines? I still like the compression check. EFI engines run as lean as the engine can bear. They are sensitive, and even small system problems can wreck the engine. Run the compression check, then do the remainder of the diagnostic procedure.

Sure, EFI engines are supposed to be diagnosed entirely with a computer. The laptop is the reigning champion and the salvation of the mechanic. The computer can tell you that the injector on the No. 4 cylinder is faulty. It can tell you if that injector is operating properly. But it cannot tell you if the manufacturer's design specifications do not fit a given application.

And, remember, pistons, rings, valves and other mechanical parts are not electronic. Their welfare is hostage to the good behavior of the electronics package and if the ECM or anything under its control should misbehave, the mechanical parts will suffer.

You will not be able to repair an ECM or other electronic module. You simply replace it.

On the most modern, fully electronic engines, the computer will relieve you of many diagnostic duties, but you can still reinforce this knowledge with a compression check.

At least 85 percent of your tune-up problems will occur in one or more areas involving the induction tract.

CHAPTER TWELVE

FLAME PROPAGATION

Entire engineering studies have been conducted on this subject alone, but I am going to try to make the elements of flame propagation understandable.

Flame propagation is the process of igniting the air/fuel mix in the cylinder and the manner in which the resulting flame spreads.

After ignition, a flame front develops and spreads across the combustion chamber. As it moves, it involves additional droplets of air/fuel mix and thus it is said to propagate. The manner in which this process develops is important.

This process of combustion has a burn rate, or the rate in parts of a second at which the mixture burns. If the burn rate is satisfactory, the piston gets a nice, smooth push. If the burn rate is excessive, there is an uncontrolled explosion in the combustion chamber.

We call this phenomenon detonation, and it is a destructive force. With detonation, temperatures rise, pressures build, valves fail, pistons may fail and bearings are destroyed.

There are three principal causes of detonation. Excessive cylinder pressure would be a simple, one-line answer, but excessive pressure is caused by other factors. High spark timing, lean mixtures and excessive loads are the most likely culprits.

Let us take them one at a time.

Begin with the piston coming up on the compression stroke. It will take a bit of time for the air/fuel mixture to reach full pressure after ignition. We want the piston to get the benefit of that maximum pressure, so we use a bit of lead in the spark timing.

The engine fires about 32 degrees before top dead center at cruising speed. The piston is still moving upward when this happens. Some of the air/fuel supply is ignited immediately and the flame front begins to spread, or propagate.

Pressure on the remaining air/fuel supply increases as the piston continues to rise. If the timing is proper, the piston will reach top dead center at the optimum moment and receive a nice even push downward.

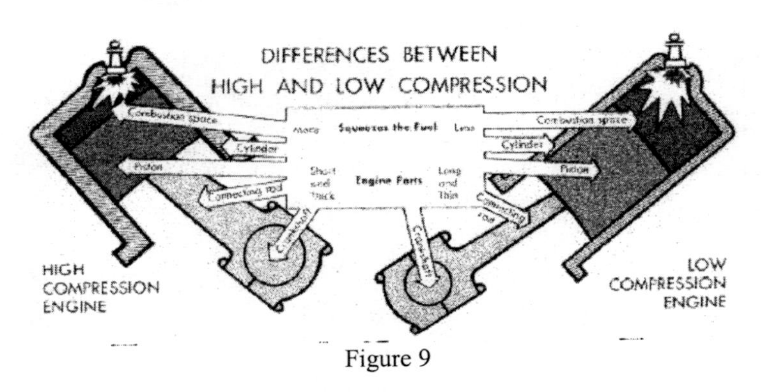

Figure 9

The difference between high and low compression.

If the timing of the spark is too early, the pressure will become excessive as the expanding gasses fight the rising piston. The flame front will begin to spread more rapidly, reacting to this excessive pressure.

The racing flame front will build a secondary pressure wave against those gasses at the periphery of the cylinder. If this pressure becomes high enough, those remote gasses will ignite and cause a secondary explosion. At this point, we have lost control.

We now have air/fuel mix burning in two locations and two pressure waves racing toward each other. Pressure builds up in the cylinder and temperatures become highly elevated. We have the makings of a full-fledged disaster.

This problem could be caused by firing the engine too early, but it can also be caused by a lean mixture. With a lean mixture, there is a larger amount of air and, therefore, more oxygen than normal in the mixture.

The entire air/fuel mix is involved almost immediately after ignition. The flame front spreads rapidly, and the entire piston top gets a high temperature smack in the face. The heat from this lean mixture can easily burn holes in the piston.

On the other hand, detonation could be caused by an overloaded engine. In this situation, the engine is straining, and the piston resists the effort of the burning fuel to push it downward. The pressure grows rapidly and, as in the first example, we get our secondary explosion.

The cures for these problems may be as simple as a change in the spark timing or the mixture, or using a smaller propeller to take some of the load off. □

The problem also could lie in the gasoline octane rating. But make sure the octane is the problem before making a change. If you are running fuel with the octane rating suggested by your manufacturer, look to other solutions first. High-octane fuel can be a help or a hindrance.

Numbers indicate the ability of a fuel to handle pressure. The higher the octane number, the slower the fuel burns at any given pressure.

High-octane fuels can resist the increased temperatures of high-compression pressures, high engine loadings and other stresses. They burn smoothly at pressures that lower octane fuels cannot accept.

Yet they are not a panacea. The high-octane fuel that

burns more slowly at higher pressures will also burn slowly at low pressures. Thus, there is no advantage in using high-octane fuel in a low-pressure engine. The fuel may not burn completely.

Moreover, a high-octane fuel can allow you to overload the engine and get away with it. The engine will not detonate and you will hear no ping, nor will you see any problems from the spark plugs. You will lose performance.

If that engine is overloaded, it is losing rpms and horsepower.

The octane rating should balance with the compression pressures and load characteristics of the engine. Generally, follow the manufacturer's recommendations.

What will I see or hear to tell me if I have a problem with detonation? That pinging sound that you sometimes hear is detonation. The idea that your valves are rattling is not an accurate description. You are, in fact, hearing a secondary explosion at the cylinder walls.

White colors or little blisters on the electrode of a spark plug indicate a lean, hot mixture. Small particles of aluminum on the electrode are pieces of your piston. □A tendency to bind when you try to crank the engine is usually caused by high timing. The engine is firing too early and fighting the starter.

When you have disassembled the engine and there is a light-colored or nearly clean ring around the outside of the piston, your engine is running in detonation. The clean area is caused by heat great enough to burn even the carbon away.

The shape of the combustion chamber has much to do with the ability of the engine to make power, resist detonation and perform efficiently. The wedge-shaped combustion chamber is normal for most gasoline-powered marine engines.

This wedge chamber is efficient for most purposes. □It has a spark plug at the tallest or highest end of the chamber. Here, at the point of greatest volume, we provide a spark plug and here we have ignition.

Pressure begins at the big end of the chamber and, as the piston moves downward, progresses toward the little end. The piston is retreating and the volume of the chamber is increasing as the flame propagates across the face of the piston. The pressure is building, of course, but it is building into an ever-increasing volume or space.

The wedge chamber is not the best shape for maximum power, but it is the best all around. The concept is sound and it works very well, within reasonable limits.

The fact that we often exceed those limits is proven by the number of early engine failures that we see every year.

The intensity of an explosion is measured by the burn rate of the explosive. Any explosive has a known burn rate. Gasoline, when mixed with air and ignited under pressure, has a burn rate greater than many of our explosives. If the engine goes into detonation, you have a problem.

THE BLOCK ASSEMBLY

The induction system is the heart, lung and brain apparatus, while the block assembly is the engine body.

Gasoline-fueled marine engines are powerful machines and their stamina is phenomenal. A 350 cubic-inch, 260 horsepower marine engine is an excellent example. This engine produces as much horsepower in its naturally aspirated form as a diesel does with a turbo charger.

Using the factory curves, let's compare a 350 cubic-inch gas block to a 354 cubic-inch diesel.

We find that the gasoline engine produces 18 percent more torque, even at 1,500 rpms, than the diesel. How about the maximum torque figures? The gas engine develops 305 lbs./ft against 258 for the diesel. Again, a substantial advantage.

The gasoline engine produces twice as much horsepower: 260 horsepower for the gas engine against 130 horsepower for the diesel.

If we add a turbocharger to the diesel, it helps, but we still see 240 horsepower for the diesel and 260 for the gasoline engine. Even with that uneven advantage, the gasoline engine is still impressive.

CHAPTER THIRTEEN

CYLINDER BLOCK

The cylinder block is the foundation of the engine. For this discussion, I will use the V-8 engine, but the same general characteristics apply with the V-6 or the in-line engine.

Because the engine block is much lighter today and casting techniques are more accurate, thin wall casting is possible.

Charles Kettering was a power at General Motors when thin wall technology was new. He observed, "We can save 35 to 50 pounds per engine with this technology."

At that time, cast iron sold for about 2 cents per pound. The maximum savings would be about $1 per engine, but when you make 8 million engines per year, the savings is significant.

The real value, of course, is in the reduced weight. In a twin-engine installation, you save 100 pounds. □That makes a difference for any vessel. The thinner walls also transfer heat to the coolant more rapidly.

The cylinder walls must not be too thin or they will bulge when the pressure of combustion is applied. The webbings in the block must still be strong enough to hold the crankshaft in line. The block scantlings must still give support.

We welcome the lighter block, but we must not sacrifice strength. Take the weight out where it is not needed and leave it in where we require it for stiffness or rigidity.

Machine work on the cylinder block tends to make or break the performance of the engine. Everything must be aligned. Begin with the crankshaft main webs. We need perfect alignment through the webbings so the crankshaft will ride easily.

The cylinder bores must be exactly concentric over the crankshaft centerlines so the pistons will be aligned with the rod bearings. The deck (top) of the block must be aligned with the crankshaft centers so the combustion chambers will have balanced volumes.

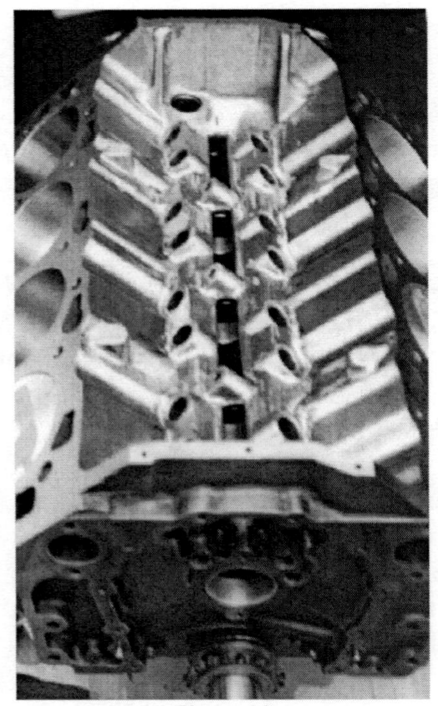

Figure 10

The rebuild process can continue in this extermely clean block.

All machine work must be accurate, which is seldom the case on a stock engine. The figures are getting better, but most stock engines have substantial misalignment in one or more parts. This is a fertile area for the hot-rodder or custom engine builder.

If you ever have the opportunity, take an engine block that has been blueprinted (made exactly accurate) and fitted with new bearings. When the crankshaft is mounted and torqued into place, turn the crankshaft by hand. The shaft just seems to float along, even though it is quite heavy.

The friction that plagued the engine before was robbing it of horsepower, and you will feel the difference when a blueprinted engine begins to operate. It does not have to be a hotrod to take advantage of blueprinting. This tidy-up can help any engine.

At the same time, do not let these misalignments scare you. The factory does a great job of mass producing reasonably priced, efficient engines that run surprisingly well. That blueprint job can cost several hundred dollars.

The cylinder block can be bored to an oversize and accept larger pistons as the engine wears. These oversizes usually come in 0.010 increments, but you can buy custom pistons at any size you care to specify.

Do not get carried away. Remember, as you increase the bore, you are taking meat out of the cylinder wall and the thickness is being reduced accordingly. Of course, when you reduce the thickness, you also reduce the stiffness and transfer heat to the coolant more rapidly. There is both a trade-off and a limit.

The cylinder block has passages that are rifle-drilled into its body. These passages, collectively called the gallery, transfer lubricating oil to the various parts of the engine. □Some of these passages are drilled into the main bearing webbings.

The crankshaft receives lubrication through the main webs and transfers it to the rod journals. Other passages drilled into the lifter holes lubricate the camshaft followers. Another set of passages feeds oil to the camshaft bearings.

Overhead valves and the rocker arms are fed by the hollow pushrods that receive oil from holes atop the lifter bodies.

The entire oiling system is an integrated delivery vehicle with some rather ingenious arrangements.

Lubricating oil is introduced to the oil gallery initially from the oil pump, which is bolted to the base of the block. This is usually a gear-type pump that can generate very high pressure. A relief valve reduces the pressure to the engine.

Excessive oil pressure can literally wash away the bearings. Many technicians and lay repairmen simply refuse to believe that oil pressure can possibly be excessive. They use a high-pressure oil pump with standard engine bearings, then wonder why they fail.

The oil pump is generally driven by a gear on the camshaft. The gear drives the distributor, which, in turn, drives the oil pump. The connection is made with an extension on the distributor shaft.

There are arrangements at the rear of the engine for a main bearing seal that holds the oil inside the crankcase. There are several types of these seals, such as rope seals and lip seals.

One of the main bearings will be designated a thrust bearing. This is usually the center main on a V-8 engine. The insert bearing for this main will have a skirt that overlaps the side of the engine. The crankshaft has a corresponding flange.

The two should mate with a limited clearance for oiling. This arrangement dictates the amount of play or end-to-end movement of the crankshaft.

The thrust bearing is important to maintain alignment between the timing gears and the timing chain.

Water passages in the cylinder block circulate water for cooling throughout the engine. Holes in the deck of the block match holes in the cylinder head and transfer coolant from the block upward to the head.

Cooling water or coolant always moves upward for two reasons: It is natural for heated water to rise, and by filling the lower areas initially and allowing the coolant to rise, you reduce the likelihood of hot spots forming in the cooling system.

The cylinder block has threaded holes in the surface to accept attachment bolts for the cylinder heads. Virtually all marine engines use cap screws threaded with NS or standard pitch.

The circulating water pump is bolted to the front of the block, and coolant enters through this pump. A pair of distribution pipes deliver a balanced flow to the cylinder banks to cool the engine evenly.

The bell housing is an oval casting that bolts to the rear of the block. It provides a cover for the flywheel and a high point for mounting the starter. It also supports the transmission. The bell housing is usually made of cast iron, but some are cast of aluminum.

One of the delights of the modern marine engine is accessibility. The starter was once mounted on the base of the block but is now atop the bell housing and is easily accessible. Oil filters, crankcase drains and other parts are on top of the engine.

The coil, distributor and wiring harness connection also sit here.

CHAPTER FOURTEEN

ROTATING ASSEMBLY

The rotating assembly consists of the crankshaft, flywheel, harmonic balancer and big ends of the connecting rods, which turn with the crankshaft and must be balanced with it.

The crankshaft may be cast from iron or forged from steel. Although the steel crankshaft is stronger, harder and more resistant to wear, it is less forgiving. An engine with a steel crankshaft must be very clean inside to take advantage of this forging.

The crankshaft emerges from either casting or forging in a rough form and it requires extensive machine work before it is ready to be assembled into the engine. All of the journals must be machined to accept their bearings.

The shaft must also be balanced (see section on Balance).

The crankshaft has a set of main bearing journals at the centerline. The crankshaft rides in the half-moon-shaped main bearings, which are half in the main webbings and half in the main bearing caps.

This type of insert bearing consists of a shell or steel backing that is the backbone for the bearing. The shell is plated with a series of metal coatings. Because there are usually three coatings, the insert is referred to as a tri-metal bearing.

The first of these coatings is usually a copper or cuprous alloy. The second is the actual bearing metal, generally an alloy, although the nature varies from bearing to bearing. Bearings for normal use tend to be rather soft and have good embedding qualities. This means small particles of impurities in the oil or stray fragments of metal will embed in the bearing itself and not scar the crankshaft.

The third coating is usually tin and will wear off in the first few miles. It is there to prevent scuff or minor dragging between bearing and crankshaft while the clearances are tight. Main bearing to journal clearances generally run about 0.002 inch when the crankshaft and bearings are new.

Bearings for high-performance use are made of harder alloys to withstand the high stress loadings of extended performance, but they are less forgiving of mistakes. Their embedding qualities are not so good and they require very clean assembly standards.

The crankshaft is hollow. Lubricating oil is delivered to the main journals through holes in the main webbings. These holes are directly drilled into the oil gallery and receive full oil pressure from the pump.

The main bearing journals have additional holes drilled from the journals into the hollow interior of the crankshaft to deliver oil to the connecting rod bearings. Centrifugal force from the spinning crankshaft enhances the lubrication.

The crankshaft has an arm that is the lever that produces torque and also changes rotating motion into reciprocating motion. The arm supports the rod journals, which, in turn, support the connecting rods.

The distance from the centerline of the rod journal to the centerline of the main journal is half the stroke because, as the crankshaft rotates 180 degrees, the arm rises and falls in a single rotation. This stroke is repeated twice in each complete revolution. This bit of information will become more meaningful in the chapter on “Balance.”

The rod journals are encircled by the big ends of the connecting rods, which retain rod bearings, another set of shells similar to those used for the main bearings.

The connecting rods for marine engines are called split rods because the big end is made in two halves to accommodate the bearing shells. These halves are retained by a pair of high-tensile steel rod bolts.

Connecting rods are subjected to unbelievable loads and stresses. That flying piston must stop at the top of the stroke and start again. It must stop at the bottom of the stroke and start again. It repeats this process, two stops and two starts, every revolution.

A set of counterweights are cast into the crankshaft body to counter the force of the piston and its parts as they go flying about in the engine.

The flywheel is bolted onto the end of the crankshaft. It turns with the crankshaft and is balanced with the crankshaft. The flywheel holds the starter ring. The starter sends energy to the flywheel through a ring gear pressed onto the outside.

The flywheel also helps the engine to run smoothly. Remember that power stroke we discussed earlier? The engine fires as the piston is rising, and some force must be employed to push the piston ahead against this pressure. Enter the flywheel.

Inertia in the flywheel is said to carry the engine through from stroke to stroke. The flywheel also absorbs the fluctuations between power pulses and smoothes out the engine operation.

The flywheel supports the flex plate, which drives the transmission. The flex plate is a metal disc about 0.0187-inch thick and about 10.5 inches in circumference. It bolts to the periphery of the flywheel.

An arbor riveted into its center is equipped with a set of internal or female splines that match another set machined into the input shaft on the transmission. These are external or male splines. The union between these splines transfers power from the engine to the transmission.

Thus, the flywheel serves many purposes and without this assembly we would be faced with a number of seemingly insurmountable problems.

There are several types of flywheels, each compatible with an individual crankshaft. If you match the wrong flywheel to the crankshaft, vibrations will destroy the crankshaft and possibly the entire engine.

The harmonic balancer is no less important to the engine. This unit supports the pulley that drives engine accessories, such as the alternator, water pump and a power steering pump for the stern drive.

CHAPTER FIFTEEN

THE PISTON/ROD ASSEMBLY

The piston and the top half, or small end of the connecting rod, are balanced together and operate in close union.

Because the small end of the connecting rod reciprocates, or moves up and down with the piston, it is considered part of the same assembly when it is time to balance the engine. The piston, a well-engineered piece of work, fills the cylinder bore. It accepts the pressure generated by burning gasses and translates that pressure into reciprocating (up and down) motion. The connecting rod transfers this pressure to the crankshaft arm.

Power first begins to be generated atop the piston. Pistons are usually made of aluminum, although they may be cast or forged.

Alloys in the aluminum vary widely from manufacturer to manufacturer, with much of the argument centered on silicone. One school of thought holds that you should allow the piston to grow under heat but leave clearance between the piston and the bore to allow for this. Others argue for limited-expansion alloys and a closer initial fit.

The piston looks round at first blush, but it is tapered

from the top, or crown, to the bottom, or skirt. It is also cam ground from side to side, producing an egg shape that allows for uneven expansion.

Cam shapes are graded alphabetically. The amount of taper in the piston body and the style of the grind vary by manufacturer.

The crown can be flat, domed, or dished. The flat-top piston is, of course, flat on top. The domed piston has a raised area on the top that protrudes into the combustion chamber to reduce combustion chamber volume and raise compression. The dished piston has a lowered area machined into its top to increase combustion chamber volume and decrease the compression ratio.

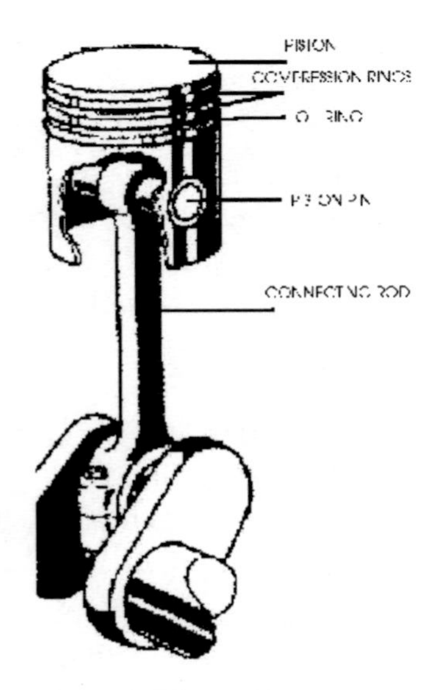

Figure 11

Typical crankshaft, piston and rod assembly.

The piston crown is the bottom portion of the combustion chamber, and each of these shapes affects not only compression ratios but also flame propagation.

Pistons may have a set of eyebrows, or half-moon incisions, which are machined at an angle into the piston crown. The eyebrow allows the piston to come to top dead center without hitting the valve, which may still be open.

The lift in the camshaft and the duration of that lift dictates whether the eyebrow is needed in any given engine assembly. Higher-lift camshafts with longer durations must have these eyebrows. Camshafts with a brief duration or small lift numbers do not require them. Many piston makers include an eyebrow, regardless of the installation, just to be safe.

The camshaft might float a lifter at any time. This could occur, for example, if the vessel should hop a wave and the engine over revs. Then the camshaft follower floats and the valve does not close on time.

The piston has a wrist pin boss cast or forged into its body. This thickening of the piston body allows for a machined hole to accept the wrist pin. The wrist pin boss is the point of greatest expansion on the body of the piston; thus, the narrow side of the egg is toward the wrist pin boss.

The wrist pin connects the piston to the connecting rod and it passes through the body of the piston. The hole where it enters the piston is called a bore. The wrist pin may enter the bore with a tight or loose fit. Wrist pins that are fit tightly into the piston have bearings only in the small end of the connecting rod.

Those with a loose fit are able to move in both the piston and connecting rod. These full floating wrist pins are seldom seen except on custom pistons for hot rods or a very few factory-built, high-performance engines.

Wrist pins with a tight fit must be pressed into their bores. Full floating wrist pins can be pushed into place with the hand.

Both use a pin lock to retain the wrist pin within the piston bores. These locks may be a wound wire type or a clip type. Full floating pins sometimes have a Teflon button that fits into the hollow end of the pin and rides on the cylinder bore. All of these pieces are designed to prevent the wrist pin from contacting the sides of the cylinders.

The amount of taper in the piston affects the skirt-to-wall clearance. This space between the piston and the cylinder bore is usually measured in thousandths of an inch. The clearance will be greater at the crown than at the skirt because the crown receives the greatest amount of heat and expands the most.

The clearance is usually measured at the skirt because the piston is generally round at the skirt. Both the taper and the cam grinding effect are ended at this point.

The remainder of the dimensions are dependent upon this measurement at the skirt. If you are fitting a set of factory pistons at stock performance figures, always use the factory dimensions. If you are fitting custom pistons, always use the manufacturer's recommendation.

Moreover, you must be certain the piston is compatible with the application, or you may be disappointed with the results.

Custom fitting a set of pistons to dimensions of your own choosing is a demanding science. If you are running a high-performance engine and you have recurring problems with the pistons, you may need professional advice.

There are two types of piston rings that serve three purposes: compression rings and oil scraper rings. These do exactly what the name implies: Compression rings seal the piston against leaks while retaining the hot gasses in the cylinders, and oil scrapers hold lubricating oil down in the crankcase and prevent leaks into the combustion chamber.

The piston rings also serve as a transfer link, passing heat from the piston to the cylinder walls. Water passages in the block cool the cylinder walls and the cylinder walls, in turn, help to cool the piston.

There is a series of lands and grooves into which the piston rings fit. They have an end gap, the space between the ends of the rings when they are installed in the cylinder bores. The measurement is taken by installing the rings squarely in the bores, without the pistons, and measuring the end gap with a feeler gauge.

This clearance must allow expansion of the ring when the temperature rises in the cylinder. The ends of the rings must still be close enough to seal and prevent leakage when the pressure of combustion hits the piston ring.

The piston rings are fit to close tolerances between ring and groove. As the engine operates, the rings and their grooves wear. Eventually, the piston, ring or both must be replaced.

The connecting rod must be stiff to accept pressure and the shock of the start/stop effort the piston will experience twice for each revolution. The rods should be the same length, and the distance from the center of the small end to the center of the big end must be the same on all the rods in a set.

Moreover, the bores of the little and big ends of the connecting rods must lie in the same geometric plane. A tool called a go-no-go gauge measures this.

The gauge begins life as a heavy, flat, steel plate, machined to true dimensions. At one end, there is a pin with an exact outside diameter to match the inside diameter of the small end of the connecting rod. At the other, there is another pin with exact outside dimensions to match the inside diameter of the bug end of the connecting rod.

These pins are spaced apart the exact distance that should appear between the big and little ends of the connecting rod. The rod that matches all of these dimensions will fit easily onto these pins and lie flat on the gauge surface. This rod will go and it is said to be straight.

In the next chapter we will put the rotating and reciprocating assemblies together and do a bit of mathematics, as well.

CHAPTER SIXTEEN

CRANK/ROD/PISTON ASSEMBLY

We have looked at individual parts; now let us look at the entire assembly. The crankshaft, connecting rods and pistons with their rings and pins are like a close-knit family in which each complements the other. If one becomes ill, they are all likely to be infected.

For lubrication alone, the connecting rod bearings, main bearings and camshaft bearings receive oil from the same source, the gallery. If a single bearing fails, the oil pressure drops and all bearings are effected. Particles from that failed bearing are likely to find their way into the common oil supply.

Then there is the matter of balance. Again, the piston, rod and crank depend upon one another.

Before we put these parts together and start them into motion, let's look at a few calculations.

MATHEMATICS

Let's start with the bore/stroke ratio. This gives the relationship between bore and stroke, expressed as a fraction or decimal. If the bore and stroke are the same, say 4.00 inches of bore diameter and 4.00 inches of stroke length, the engine is said to be square.

If the bore is greater than the stroke, the engine is oversquare. If the bore is less than the stroke, the engine is undersquare. Almost all modern engines made in the United States are slightly to moderately oversquare.

Some European and a few Japanese engines are undersquare.

If we divide the bore into the stroke, we get a good indication of the relationship between the two. □Square engines will have the number 1. Oversquare engines will have a fraction less than 1. Consider an engine with a 4-inch bore and a 3.48-inch stroke. Dividing 4 into 3.48 gives us 0.87.

This, in fact, is the bore stroke ratio for our 350 cubic-inch sample engine. This type engine is probably the most popular power plant ever placed in a boat. It is generally considered to be a free-revving, high-output engine, with a good power band. If the stroke were longer, it might not turn so freely, but it could develop more torque on the low end.

Now let us discuss the crankshaft. The crankshaft arm is half the length of the stroke. Multiply the length of the arm by 2 and you have the length of the stroke. Now, again multiply the stroke by 2 and you have the figure for piston travel in one revolution.

Why is this important? When we have determined the piston travel for a single revolution, we can multiply by the rpms and get a number for piston speed. If we divide the result by 12, we convert the figure from inches to feet and now we have a piston speed in feet per minute.

The formula actually looks like this:

$$S \times 2 \times rpms / 12 = PS$$

In this model, S is the stroke in inches, rpms are the revolutions per minute and PS is the piston speed. Let us try this with our 350 cubic-inch engine at 3,000 rpms. We know the stroke is 3.48 inches; multiply this by 2. We now have 6.96 inches multiplied by 3,000 rpms.

The result is 20,880 inches, divided by 12. This yields a figure of 1,740 feet per minute in piston speed.

This is important because it speaks to the matter of piston ring wear. That engine is dragging the piston rings up and down the bores for a distance of roughly one mile for each three minutes of operation.

The longer the stroke, the more piston and ring wear for every revolution. The shorter the stroke, the less ring wear.

If ring wear were the only consideration, we would prefer a short-stroke engine.

Let us consider another calculation. Remember the piston starts and stops twice for each revolution. The energy contained in that moving piston is described as kinetic energy, which means energy in motion.

Kinetic energy is calculated according to the formula $KE=MV^2$. In this model, kinetic energy is equal to the Mass (weight) multiplied by the square of the velocity at the time the piston stops.

How severe is this kinetic load?

In 1952 I read an estimate offered by an engineer from the Chrysler Corp. suggesting that it required 5 tons of pressure to stop the piston from a 392 Hemi engine and start it again. The power lost in making these starts and stops is substantial.

Kinetics imposes high loads on the bearings and crankshaft The pressure that starts and stops the pistons must be carried by rod bearings and main bearings, sometimes for hours.

Let's juggle the bore/stroke numbers for a mythical engine. The longer-stroke engine has higher piston speeds and naturally it has higher kinetic losses.

Again, this situation would also seem to suggest that a short-stroke engine is the better choice. □But what happens to our torque figures? As we shorten that arm, we reduce the torque figures dramatically.

To avoid losing our torque figures, we can add length to the torque arm and cut back on the rpms.

But, if we keep the same number of cubic inches and add length to the stroke, we must then reduce the bore diameter. When we do that, we do two questionable things at once. We reduce the number of square inches of piston surface, which, in turn, reduces the total pressure on the crankshaft arm.

We also reduce the size of the cylinder and the space available for intake and exhaust valves. In that smaller cylinder, we must reduce our valve sizes, and this cuts down on our breathing. Now the cylinder pressure will fall even further.

Juggling the figures is a matter of compromise. The final figures for engine dimensions must consider the purpose for which the engine is intended and the engine must then be designed accordingly. And because each thing on the engine is dependent upon the others, every change affects the entire engine. The factory engine is well designed. Be certain you know what you are doing before you begin to experiment.

Consider this: Back in the 1950s, the Jaguar company built an automobile engine with about 4.5 liters of piston displacement. The engine made around 255 horsepower at something close to 6,000 rpms.

The designers needed a smaller engine for a baby version of one of their models and they decided to alter the 4.5. They would cut the engine down from 4.5 liters to 2.8 liters by reducing the stroke alone. They cut the stroke about 1 full inch, lowered the deck on the cylinder block but kept the same cylinder head, valves and pistons.

The engine was expected to lose about 100 horsepower and come in at 155 or thereabouts. In actual operation that 2.8 engine revved freely all the way to 8,000 rpms. The horsepower was almost exactly 255. The first 2.8 liter engines were nearly identical to the 4.5 liter in output.

The shorter stroke and lower kinetics made a huge contribution to this result. The smaller engine now had valves that were larger in relation to the cylinder displacement and the engine could really breathe. It lost a whole bunch of low end torque due to the shorter crankshaft arm but that baby would really wail.

It had to turn much higher than the 4.5 liter power plant to get the horsepower but turn it did and nobody predicted the results. Nobody.

CHAPTER SEVENTEEN

FOUR QUADRANTS

We are going to divide crankshaft travel into four quadrants and use this division to show changing relationships.

First, think about the arm on the crankshaft. That arm rotates and the rod journal describes a complete circle for each revolution. You are looking at the crankshaft from the timing gear end of the engine.

As the engine rotates, the crankshaft will describe a 360-degree circle. Divide that circle into quadrants. The first line will run from top to bottom, passing through the top dead center and bottom dead center positions on the crankshaft.

The second line will pass across the circle at right angles to the first line. We now have the circle divided into four points at 0, 90, 180 and 270 degrees.

At 0, we have the beginning of all events in the crankshaft cycle. All timing of the engine begins here. The camshaft, valve action and spark timing relate to this mark.

The 180-degree mark is at bottom dead center, the 90-degree mark is exactly perpendicular to the center line on the right side and the 270-degree mark is perpendicular to the center line on the left side.

Visualize the crankshaft as it passes over that 0, or top dead center, mark. The crankshaft arm is almost straight up and any pressure exerted upon the piston is pushing straight down, with no developed torque.

Pressure at this time is wasted. We call this dead travel in the crankshaft. It lasts for about 5 crankshaft degrees, 2.5 degrees on each side of the 0 mark.

As the crankshaft continues to rotate, the angle on the arm increases and the developed torque begins to rise. □Pressure on the arm is being translated into twisting motion and this is translated into rotation.

As the crankshaft descends, the angle will increase until the shaft reaches 90 degrees. The faster this angle changes, the faster the piston moves.

The speed of the piston increases for every degree the crankshaft turns in the first quadrant.

As the piston approaches bottom dead center, the reverse takes place. The piston moves less and less for every degree the crankshaft turns. The angle between crankshaft and piston is decreasing and soon they will be in a straight line, relative to each other.

In the third quadrant, the piston is past bottom dead center and rising. Again, we had a 5-degree dead space at bottom dead center during which the piston does not move with the crankshaft. Then the piston moves at an increasing speed, relative to the degrees of crankshaft travel. The angle between piston and crankshaft grows.

This continues until the crankshaft reaches the 270-degree mark and the situation reverses itself.

Thus, we see that in quadrants 1 and 3, the relationship between crankshaft movement and piston travel increases. In quadrants 2 and 4, the relationship is reversed.

All of this affects design.

The amount of air/fuel mix the engine demands increases as the piston travels down in that first quadrant. Valve openings and flow characteristics must recognize this need.

To make any calculations, I have to know what the

volume of the cylinder is at any given spot in the crankshaft travel. I have to know how fast the engine is turning and how fast the piston will move for the next degree of crankshaft travel.

Then I need to know what the volume of the cylinder will be after the piston moves for that single degree of crankshaft travel. The difference between these two figures can be translated into demand for air/fuel mix at a given speed.

Now I can address valve sizes, camshaft lift, manifold diameters, venturi diameter and jet sizes just to estimate flow for a single degree of crankshaft travel on the intake stroke.

On the power stroke, we see another problem. Pressure from the burning charge is greatest at top dead center when the crankshaft arm is nearly vertical and makes the least torque. As the crankshaft rotates, the cylinder pressure falls. □That single charge of air/fuel mix that we burned in the cylinder is losing pressure.

The crankshaft arm, however, becomes more effective as it turns. The engine will have an increasing potential to produce torque as the crankshaft approaches 90 degrees. The angle between piston and crankshaft arm will be best for the production of torque as pressure on the piston is running out.

The next consideration is piston travel and rod angularity. Consider that the piston moves in a straight line, up and down. The wrist pin follows that line. Rod angularity is the angle between the line of piston travel and the connecting rod journal.

The more acute this angle becomes, the less pressure is transferred from the piston to the crankshaft. The less acute or the straighter this angle, the more pressure is transferred. It becomes obvious that a short rod will produce a very acute angle with less torque.

A long rod will produce a much straighter angle with greater pressure transfer and more torque produced. The problem is easy to see: A long rod will require the engine block be deeper and heavier. The long rod will be easier to bend but it is more efficient.

The short rod will produce less torque for a unit of pressure but the block can be lower and lighter. The short rod is stiffer and less likely to bend or break. Also the short rod with its lighter loading tends to wrap up (accelerate) faster than the long rod.

What are we to do? Save iron, add acceleration and keep the rod short or increase the deck height of the block, add more iron and increase both torque and efficiency? This is an ongoing argument among engine builders.

In the world of high performance engines where people tailor the crankshaft/rod assembly to specific needs, the stroke of the engine and the length of the rod are shuffled continuously for different applications. The man who shuffles best generally wins.

The dead travel losses, the inertia losses and the rod angle losses, all are detailed here and all have an adverse effect on the engines performance. We know these ills exist but we do not know how to cure them.

In fact, no one has ever been able to solve these problems in an internal combustion engine. They are problems which cause serious energy losses in the engine and contribute to the dismal efficiency numbers with which we are faced. How much energy do we really lose in the change from fuel to horsepower? That is a shocker.

The very best of our gasoline engines is about 19 percent to 20 percent efficient. Yes, we waste roughly 80 percent of our gasoline in the effort to convert fuel to useable power. This in the sense of atomic conversion.

Using the BTUs of heat energy in a gallon of gasoline versus the horsepower produced by burning it in an engine gives a figure we call, “Thermal efficiency.” That figure yields a fraction less than 1/5th. We lose 4 gallons of gasoline out of every 5 we burn in the engine.

This is a terrible waste. There must be a better way but, thus far it has not emerged.

Where does all that fuel go? That is a considerable part of the exercise we have just finished. Remember those starts and stops at top dead center and bottom dead center? That is where the kinetic losses occur.

The dead travel at top dead center absorbs a good deal of our fuel and that slowly changing angle between piston and crankshaft arm keeps torque production at a minimum while the strongest pressure from the burning fuel is being lost. But there is much more.

An enormous amount of fuel goes to cooling losses. Cooling losses occur when we circulate water or coolant through the engine. This absorbs many thousands of BTUs of heat energy and it wastes large quantities of fuel. Of course we have no choice but to cool the engine or it would be destroyed.

The friction losses from bearings, piston rings and gears is substantial. The accessories we drive, 4 horsepower to drive the oil pump, twelve horsepower for a camshaft; all of these things require a portion of the fuel we burn.

Regardless of the many negatives that occur, the engine is still a marvel of engineering and it is a source of great pleasure to many boaters. It also does a lot of commercial work. No one can estimate how many steps or lifts it has spared mankind.

If you can think of a better way you will be remembered throughout history but otherwise we will have to struggle along with what we have.

CHAPTER EIGHTEEN

BALANCE THE ENGINE

There are two forces operating in the engine. One is rotary and it is generated by the rotating mass weights. The second is linear and it is generated by the reciprocating mass weights. We are able to balance the rotating elements in the engine, but we cannot balance reciprocating elements in the engine; these we must counter balance. Forces generated by the reciprocating mass weights are not going to go away because they have been countered. In fact, quite the opposite is true.

These forces are counter balanced by generating an equal force which acts in the opposite direction. Look carefully at the crankshaft and you will notice the counter weights cast into the crankshaft. They are on the side of the crankshaft opposite the piston.

The piston goes up and the counter weight goes down. The piston hits top dead center and it jerks to a momentary stop. The counter weight hits bottom dead center at exactly the same instant and it jerks to a stop. Each moving weight creates an equal force, applied in opposite directions.

The crankshaft accepts this double load and we feel very little. The piston, piston rings wrist pin, pin locks and the small end of the connecting rod, plus a portion of the rod itself are weighed with the reciprocating mass, to be countered by the swinging counter weight.

Now consider the alignment of these forces. The counter weight may generate an exact duplicate of the force it will counter but these forces are not exactly in a line. The counter weight is slightly off center from the connecting rod. Thus these forces load the crankshaft in an uneven manner.

Moreover, the force and counter force are only in balance or counter at two points in the engine's rotation, at top dead center and at bottom dead center. At all other positions of the crankshaft, approximately 350 degrees out of a total of 360 degrees of rotation, the counter weight is not doing its intended job.

In fact, it is misaligned from and completely off center to the line in which the piston travels, thus the force generated by the counterweight is not actually effecting the piston. Now we must find a way to counter the effects of the counterweight itself.

We have all these additional counter weights, one for each piston, distributed evenly around the crank. If we keep all of these evenly distributed counterweights to the same weight themselves, they will balance each other, right?

Sure but the forces will be offset since the weights are in different positions along the length of the crankshaft. Again we get that uneven load on the crankshaft. It becomes rather obvious that there are numerous unaligned forces working around the crankshaft, all trying to tear it apart.

As a result of all these misaligned forces, each working against the other, there are numerous vibrational elements generated by the moving parts of the engine. It is to be expected that some patterns will emerge.

Different elements of the engine will develop their own vibrational components. Pistons for example are responsible for what is known as "second order vibrations." There are many other different vibrational elements present.

I will not start a long complicated dissertation on the subject of vibration but there are a few things I want you to understand. Every piece of metal in the engine has a critical vibration frequency, at which it will fail.

You can see the principal at work when a singer with a very powerful voice hits just the right note and a water glass shatters before your eyes. The vibrations generated by the voice of the singer reverberate at exactly the right pitch or frequency and the glass is destroyed.

At certain vibration frequencies, the valve springs will collapse, the piston rings will lose their tension and the crankshaft will break. Vibration is a very poor bedfellow. We cannot eliminate it so we try to offset its effects. We build a harmonic balancer.

This assembly goes on the crankshaft at the timing gear end and it is designed to break up vibration patterns with a known, destructive, frequency. On some engines the harmonic vibrations are pretty tough and distributed down the length of the engine. To control these vibrations, we add a balance shaft.

This shafts runs down the sides of the engine block and it, too, breaks up destructive vibration frequencies. One engine which employs this type of damper is the late style V-6 Chevrolet Marine block. This 4.3 liter power plant benefits greatly from the effects of the balance shaft.

The balance shaft resembles a camshaft in design and it has weights which are not unlike the lobes on the camshaft distributed up and down its length. Those weights generate the forces which help to break up the destructive vibrations generated by the operation of the engine.

How bad are the vibrations in a normal engine? I will tell you a quick story to illustrate this point. A few years back a well known engine manufacturer developed a four cylinder engine that looked great and ran like a champ. The engine was a winner but it had one small flaw.

If it ran at exactly 5,200 rpms for 30 continuous seconds it would break the crankshaft. This was no small problem. Not many of the engines suffered this destructive fate but enough did that the manufacturer redesigned the crankshaft.

The changes made to the crankshaft were not drastic but rather simple. The result was dramatic and I am still running one of those later model, redesigned engines today.

Every engine maker is quite conscious of the need to allow for the balance problems in every engine they sell.

Replacement parts are built to close tolerances and weight is one of those considerations. If you buy an oversized piston for a rebore job you may be surprised to find the weight has been held very close to that of the original piston, regardless of the larger size. Of course, this is done to prevent balance problems.

We have said a great deal, about counter balance and reciprocating mass, how about rotary balance and rotating mass? This is perhaps easier. The effort to balance the rotating mass consists of creating an even distribution of weight, all around the center of rotation.

The crankshaft, the big end of the connecting rod, the rod bearings and a portion of the connecting rod itself are included in the rotating mass. They are balanced according to those laws of even distribution I mentioned a moment ago.

Yet these parts are still not exactly aligned with each other as I stated earlier in this chapter and the effects of these misaligned forces will always be a consideration

For a balance job to really be complete it must include the flywheel, flex plate and harmonic balancer as part of the rotating mass. All of these elements must be balanced together and run on the balance machine at the same time.

Custom balanced engines are produced by many engine makers. They employ highly sophisticated techniques and very expensive machinery to accomplish this purpose. A custom balance job is an important part of any engine that will turn high rpms.

The factory work is quite sufficient for any stock engine. With the advent of Computer Assisted Manufacturing (CAM) techniques the tolerances for mass produced machine parts has been tightened up to a surprising degree.

I did not write this section to give a highly detailed description of balance or of vibration itself. I hope when you have finished reading this treatise you will understand the general nature of vibration and its sources within the engine.

I would be most gratified if you were able to visualize the moving crankshaft with the rotating and reciprocating masses in motion. I would further like to believe you can visualize those offset or non-aligned forces developing and effecting the crankshaft.

Most of the mathematics used in crankshaft design and balance are actually done by a Computer Assisted Design (CAD) system. The computer can design the parts, balance the assembly and run the engine when it is finished.

At one time the designer was faced with complicated differential equations that took hours to resolve, just to calculate the dividing length of the connecting rod. Which portion of the connecting rod is to be balanced with the reciprocating mass weights and with the rotating mass weights? Today, the computer knows.

It is quite enough for you to know, in simple terms, how the system works and why it works. If you understand that then this chapter is a success.

CHAPTER NINETEEN

THE TRANSMISSION

The transmission transmits power from the engine to the propeller shaft. It provides us with a direction change from forward to reverse and reverse to forward. It also has a neutral position so we may idle the engine without movement.

If it is properly installed it has a start-in-gear switch which breaks the continuity from the starter switch to the starter solenoid, thus making it impossible to crank the engine, except in neutral. This is a very important safety device.

Within the basic transmission, is a set of clutches for each direction the transmission must run. One set of forward clutches and one set of reverse clutches. Different transmissions employ different numbers of clutches and differing arrangements of the gears.

The twin-disc transmission, for example employs a single, large-diameter disc for its forward drive and another single, large-diameter disc for its reverse drive. The Borg Warner transmission employs a clutch pack with numerous drive discs and driven discs for each direction, forward and reverse.

The discs may have fiber faces of friction surfaces or metallic faces. Clutches with a fiber face are considered "standard" fare on many types of transmissions while their metallic faced counterparts are considered heavy duty parts.

An oil pump is designed into the transmission. It is driven at all times, even in neutral, by the input shaft. This pump delivers oil, under pressure, to apply the clutches. It also delivers oil to the moving parts for lubrication.

There are two basic configurations for the transmission, the straight drive and the V-drive. The straight drive is just what the name implies. The transmission is directly behind the engine and facing the prop shaft. The timing-gear end of the engine is facing forward.

Courtesy of Detroit Diesel
Figure 12

Straight drive marine gear.

The V-drive has an engine with the timing gear facing aft in the vessel. The transmission is attached to the bell housing as before but both are now facing forward, towards the bow. The transmission provides power to a V-drive gear box.

This gear box has an output shaft which faces back towards the stern of the vessel. Visualize an engine which appears to be installed backwards with a shaft coming from beneath the engine and reaching towards the stern, as before.

The engine/drive system literally describes a V in the bilges of the vessel. Why bother? This system allows the engines to be installed farther aft in the vessel. It allows a designer to alter the shape, balance and accommodations in the vessel. It provides flexibility and it is responsible for a few truly unique concepts.

There are many V-drive systems found in houseboats with the engine mounted very near the transom. This allows the aft deck to be utilized as an access area and makes it easier to utilize the full interior for other purposes.

Besides a direction change, what does a transmission do?

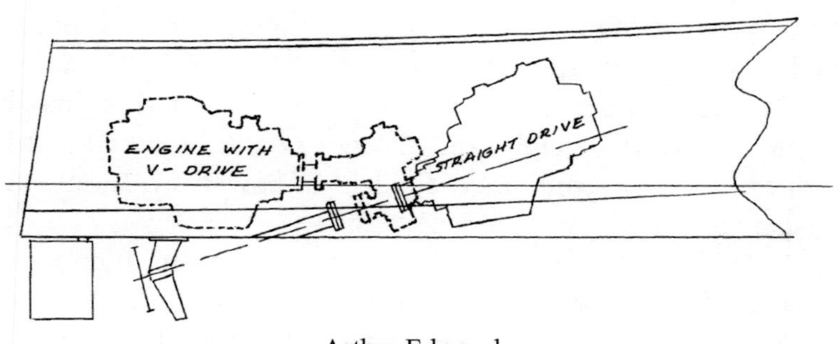

Arthur Edmunds
Figure 13

V-drive and straight drive placement.

The transmission does not change horsepower but rather the manner in which it is delivered. There are several possibilities. The transmission may return one revolution at the output shaft for every revolution which the engine provides at the input shaft.

Such a gear is said to have a 1:1 ratio. If the input shaft provides more revolutions than the output shaft the transmission is considered to be a reduction gear. It reduces the output revolutions in relation to the input revolutions. Numbers for these gears would be 1.5:1, 2:1 or a similar number.

If the transmission has more revolutions at the output shaft than at the input, the transmission is said to be an overdrive gear. The numbers for an overdriven gear set would be 1:1.5, 1:2 or a similar number.

The first digits to the left are the input revolutions while those on the right are the output revolutions. The transmission changes the rate at which work is done by the engine but it cannot change the amount of work the engine can do. Let us do a bit of math.

We begin with horsepower which is the unit by which we measure the engine's ability to do work. It is equal to 33,000 foot pounds of work, per minute. Notice carefully the element of time which is a part of this description. There is another way to state this situation.

One horsepower will lift 33,000 pounds one foot in one minute. Notice the weight, the distance and the time quotient. Each of these is an important element of power measurement. We can vary any figure in the equation.

In fact, we can even change more than one figure but when we do the horsepower will be effected accordingly. Let me give you an example. If we change the weight from 33,000 pounds to 16,500 pounds, we can raise this weight 2 feet, in one minute.

We will still accomplish 33,000 foot pounds of work. We have halved the weight to be lifted, so we can double the height to which we can lift the weight. The same rules apply to any part of the equation, it will change according to the laws of ratio and proportion.

The next bit of mathematics we are concerned with is the matter of gears and gear ratios. Let us continue with our one horsepower engine. For the sake of this demonstration, let us further assume the engine develops this horsepower at 4,000 rpms.

Using the formula we developed early:

Torque x rpms / 5252 = Horsepower

We find that this engine should develop 1.313 lbs./ft of torque. Multiply this by 4,000 rpms, divide by 5252 and we get one horsepower.

Let us then assume a transmission with a 2:1 gear reduction. The output shaft on this gear system will turn one time for each two revolutions of the input shaft. It will also multiply torque by a factor of 2 (the shaft speed is halved, the torque is double).

Running our engine at full throttle will deliver 4,000 rpms to the input shaft of the transmission. Those 4,000 rpms will be reduced by half and we now have only 2,000 rpms at the output shaft. How about the torque? Just multiply by two.

Now we have 2.626 lbs./ft. of torque. How about horsepower? Well, let us try the formula again. We have 2.626 lbs./ft. of torque which we will multiply by 2,000 .rpms. The result is 5252 and we divide this by the constant 5252. The horsepower is still One.

We can reduce or increase the rpms and the torque figure will vary proportionately. The horsepower will remain unchanged. A gear cannot change horsepower. There will always be small frictional losses in the gear itself. Yet, horsepower at the output shaft will be essentially the same as it is at the input shaft, less only those small gear losses.

Why bother with the gear? The gear ratio dictates the size of the propeller we can turn. It may be advantageous to turn a larger propeller and we want a reduction gear to allow us to do so. It may be better to turn a smaller propeller and the gear makes this feasible also.

The gear has one definite advantage in its ability to tailor engine performance to a need. Assume you have an engine that produces sufficient horsepower but is a small displacement engine. It will have to turn high rpms to get that horsepower.

The high rpm engine may be lacking in low end torque and you need to pull a good sized propeller. What to do? Get a reduction gear and increase your torque figures accordingly.

Of course, this is not going to relieve the high rpms engine from the loads imposed by stressing its small frame. It will still be loaded but it can do the job. Without a reduction gear it cannot. The reduction gear can even save that small power plant from destruction, to some extent. Remember the chapter on flame propagation and the detonation that occurs when resistance against the piston becomes too great?

A reduction gear can alleviate the probability of detonation by reducing the effort required to turn the input shaft. This reduces the resistance at the piston and allows the fuel to burn evenly and the flame front to propagate normally.

Let me be very clear on this next hypothesis. Ideally, the marine engine should have a broad torque band with high torque in the lower rpm ranges. It requires this broad torque band because the load is constant.

Briefly, consider the motorcycle engine. It is pipey in the extreme, has a short stroke, produces comparatively low torque numbers at low rpms and yet it will accelerate at tremendous speeds. The answer to this lies in multiple gears to tailor the load on the engine.

If the marine engine had a six-speed transmission to manage the torque requirements it would be a different ball game but it does not. Our marine engine must operate throughout a broad band of rpms with no gear to multiply torque. This is the true reason why high torque characteristics are so important to the marine engine.

We have thrashed out the matter of reduction gears

rather thoroughly but what if we want the propeller to turn faster? Reduction gears reduce output revolutions in relation to input revolutions, now consider the overdrive.

Overdrive gears do just the opposite. You are probably wondering what their purpose can be? I will give you an example: after World War II the big, liquid cooled, Allison Aircraft engines were very popular with the Unlimited Hydroplane builders.

These engines were huge. If I remember correctly there was a 1,150 cubic-inch engine and a larger 1,710 cubic-inch engine. Both these engines had massive displacement and they were designed to turn the large diameter propellers for the Mustangs and the Lightnings.

In a hydroplane they would have driven propellers of enormous diameter with impractical sizes and terrible drag coefficients. The overdrive gears designed for this engine made the whole thing work. They were extreme designs but they did a superb job.

They had gear ratios on the order of 1:4.5. Modified versions of the engine itself turned about 4,000 rpms and the propellers turned closer to 18,000 rpms. Sounds a bit wild but it worked. In fact, hydroplanes with a setup similar to this, set several world speed records.

What I want you to understand about this situation is twofold. First, the gear cannot change horsepower but second, it can change the rate of delivery. This means you can tailor the torque/ horsepower relationship with a transmission.

At least you can do so within the limits of the horsepower available from the engine.

CHAPTER TWENTY

THE PROPELLER AS A GOVERNOR

It is not my intention to begin a journey into the area of propeller selection but simply to discuss the impact propellers have upon the engine. The propeller decides the amount of load the engine will feel. They can make or break engine performance.

It is unfortunate we cannot easily change propeller pitch as the engine runs. We could have one pitch for acceleration, another for towing and a third for top speed. With this combination we could maintain optimum performance for a number of situations.

Aircraft propellers have been manufactured with a variable pitch and this is a most satisfactory system for airplanes but no one has developed a widely accepted unit for boats. At this writing we are more or less bound to the use of a single propeller of fixed dimensions.

There are three dimensions for any propeller which generally decide its performance. The diameter, the pitch and the blade area. The blade area varies with the design of the blades and with the number of blades.

If you look at the blades on the various inboard propellers you will notice the blades have a regular smorgasbord of shapes and twists to the blades. Each of these is designed to manage water flow and load the engine in a different manner.

The diameter and pitch of a propeller is given in inches. The diameter is always stated first and the pitch last. Thus a 14 x 15 propeller would have a diameter of 14 inches and a pitch of 15 inches. The diameter is equal to a circle which would be described by the tips of the blades in one revolution.

The pitch is equal to the distance which the blade would advance, in one revolution, assuming no slip. This is not easily determined since the blade itself has a variable pitch. That is to say the blade has a different pitch at the hub from that at the blade tips.

The propeller is changing pitch along the entire length of the blade from hub to tip. For this reason, we give the figure for pitch from a chart which measures average figures at different points on the blade.

We then calculate the average pitch and this is the figure you see in the manufacturers specifications. The diameter is an exact figure but the pitch is a composite number and as such, not exactly the same from manufacturer to manufacturer.

The late Allen Smith from Shreveport, Louisiana built many of my racing propellers. He once sent me three different blades for the B hydroplane, all marked 7-3/4 x 9. On the pitch meter they all measured to these specifications. Yet the performance was dramatically different for each blade. When you see dimension figures for any propeller, use them as a reference point and remember those reference points will be most accurate when you are using blades from the same manufacturer. Even then, they may vary.

A propeller with the same numbers for diameter and pitch is said to be square. If the diameter is greater than the pitch it is said to be over square. If the diameter is less than the pitch it is said to be under square.

How does this relate to engine performance? The propeller controls the amount of loading the engine feels at all times. It can maintain a happy power plant that is still alive after thousands of hours or it can turn a young engine into a tired wreck, overnight.

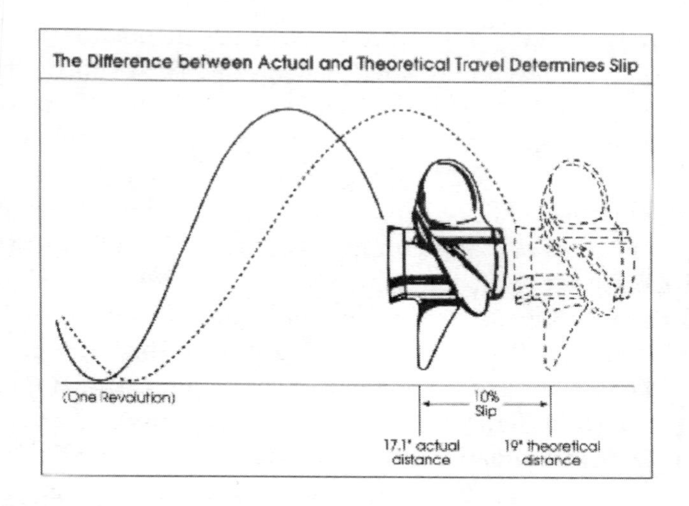

Courtesy of Mercury Marine
Figure 14

The properly designed propeller will load the engine to its exact, maximum, factory rated rpms atthe load the vessel is intended to carry. If the engine cannot turn full rpms there will be a horsepower loss, at all rpms, throughout the range.

Read the engine manufacturer's horsepower curve. If the curve calls for 260 horsepower at 4,450 rpms and your propeller loads the engine to a point it can only turn 4,000 rpms you can only get 0.898 percent of the advertised horsepower from the engine.

This is a loss of slightly over 26 horsepower. Greater overloads would produce greater losses and this condition exists through out the entire rpm range. Moreover, there is the matter of efficiency. This overload causes slow flow in the manifold runners.

The throttle butterfly is opened further than would normally be necessary but the engine cannot turn at normal speeds. The pressure in the manifold climbs and the flows slow down. Now we get puddling in the manifold and intake ports.

If the overload is great we will get detonation in the engine. We already know what that means, so we must start from a propeller that loads the engine to its proper rated speed. What about engines used for both running and towing? They are special.

You must still use a propeller that will allow the engine to turn full rpms at maximum load and when the load is gone, drive the engine with the tachometer. The entire vessel will lose some performance and be less efficient when the vessel is unloaded but it will still do fine, if you stay off the throttle.

The alternative is an overloaded engine that cannot tow effectively and will most likely destroy itself. One of the prime examples of this situation is the ski boat. It is expected to pull two or more skiers from a deep water start and it really needs a load type propeller to accomplish this purpose.

Once those skiers are finished and have climbed aboard the vessel load changes dramatically. Now you must watch the tachometer and drive the boat at cruise rpms, even though you know very well the engine is capable of much greater speed.

You are losing fuel efficiency but at least you are still riding. If you were loaded too heavily during the ski towing operation you might now be under tow yourself. There is a definite tradeoff.

Trucks and automobiles make this same type of load change by using a variety of gear ratios in a transmission but a boat has no such arrangement. We must do whatever is necessary. That means a slower ride at one point in order to tow efficiently in another.

Allen Smith once told me, "Boy, propellers are a

voodoo science. Nobody understands propellers and that includes me." His propellers held numerous speed records for both A. P. B. A. and N. O. A. boats, yet he still recognized the inexact nature of the science.

High speed, underwater cameras and Computer Assisted Design units have added a great deal to our knowledge of propellers and their application but we still have much to learn. Those of us who would make recommendations to others have the greatest task facing us today.

There are many propellers out there with very sophisticated designs for us to choose. Yet I find an unbelievable number of boats on the water with mismatched engine/propeller combinations. This is sometimes the fault of intransigent skipper/owners but it is frequently the result of poor advice. Learn all you can about the subject of propellers if this is to be your chosen vocation or avocation.

Throughout this book we have stressed the interdependency of the engine parts and assemblies, describing how one depends upon the other. That relationship extends to the final part of the drive system -- the propeller.

CHAPTER TWENTY-ONE

DURABILITY

I want you to understand the elements of durability and those factors which most effect engine life. The greatest of these are engine loading, speed of operation and maintenance.

We have already dealt with the question of proper engine loading in several areas of this book. This is important but I believe we have thoroughly explored the subject. Let us approach the matter of speed. Speed is destructive.

Begin with the engineer who designed the engine and the manufacturer who built it. Each intended the engine to conform to minimum industry standards which suggest the engine should run about 300 hours at full load and full throttle.

The same standard says the engine should run about 2,000 hours at cruising speed. There is no exact figure for what cruising speed is really. In fact, each of these measurements is a kind of understanding rather than any formal agreement.

How does speed effect these expectations of longevity? The simple difference between the 300 hour, full load, rating and the 2,000 hour expectation for cruising speeds shows a difference of almost seven to one.

Cruise rpms for the 350 cubic-inch Merc Cruiser engine are between 2,800 rpms and 3,000 rpms. The small difference between this speed and wide open throttle at 4,450 rpms is about a 50 percent increase.

Yet, the life of the engine is reduced by a factor of seven. In the reverse situation, what can be accomplished with a reduction in speed? I will offer you a real life example. In 1991 I was at the Chevrolet plant looking at a 454 cubic-inch Chevrolet engine which was operating on natural gas at a governed 1450 rpms.

This engine was set up for longevity. It developed 90 horsepower, it pulled a generator and it ran day and night without fail. The engineer who developed the system designed it for use in school buildings in remote parts of Alaska. His name was Don Weiderhold.

Don told me the 454 had no unusual parts or pieces other than the carburetor system which handled compressed gas. So what is unusual about this? At 1450 rpms, that engine had run 26,000 hours without a major repair. Few diesels get that kind of longevity.

The combination of a clean fuel and low stresses allowed the engine to last far longer than anything we normally expect. What is it that makes extended rpms so damaging to the engine? Let us go back to those early principles I discussed.

First, we know kinetics are a problem for the engine. The energy losses and bearing loads that occur as the pistons are started and stopped have been documented in these pages but how about the valve train? Those cam followers are moving up and down also.

They impose ever greater loads upon the valve springs as the speed increases and inertia tries to keep them moving. The push rods add their weight to the inertia forces in the valve train and valve spring capabilities become marginal.

The rocker arms become disproportionately harder to control and the cam followers try to float off the camshaft. They return with a sudden impact that is destructive. Even a roller tappet will destroy the camshaft if the roller itself floats instead of following the cam profile.

Add a heavy duty, high tension valve spring? Sure, you can do that but the loads on the cam lobes and the rocker arm bearings or ball/socket increase accordingly. The cam lobe wears much faster and that rocker arm stud may be jacked right out of the head if it is not screwed in.

We have seen the parts of the engine are interdependent for their welfare and if one part suffers, each will suffer. The more we visit the various parts of construction and operation, the more we find this to be true.

The vibrations generated in the engine become stronger and more destructive themselves, to an ever greater degree as speed increases. The engine goes into dangerous territory as the rpms rise. If you do not exceed the manufacturers rated maximum rpms it will run for a while, yet the life will be drastically reduced.

What is the significance of all this? First, of course, is the fact that high speed or over speed should be avoided except in cases of extreme emergency. The second lesson to be learned is that you should select an engine that will provide all the power you require while running at cruising speed.

The mariner should be aware of this and the mechanic or salesman should always present this fact to a prospect. The knowledge will serve the mariner well in making future engine choices or selecting a new vessel.

The knowledge will allow the salesman or mechanic to present a realistic set of options to a prospective purchaser. In the matter of choosing an engine, there is one anomaly you should be aware of: Some boaters really expect to run a boat on the edge.

There are those who want an engine to go fast. The life of that engine is a secondary consideration. They are willing to pay whatever cost arises to enjoy the sensation of speed.

One of my friends is running a cigarette style hull with a 502 Chevy aboard. The engine develops 850 horsepower with a 13-pound boost. It requires C-12 racing gasoline at $2.63 per gallon. It has a normal life of 88 to 100 hours before overhaul.

The outdrive generally goes out at about the same time. The engine and the total cost is near $25,000. That suits him fine. He will pay the cost to enjoy the ride.

How about maintenance? There are several reasons why maintenance is important. Maintenance includes such items as paint and finish. This is more than a beauty treatment, though appearance is important as well. The valve covers, timing cover and crankcase pan will deteriorate without upkeep.

Loose belts may squeak but they will also rag out and break, at undesirable moments. Water hoses should be changed periodically and those water pump impellers should be inspected at regular intervals. Check your gauges periodically for accuracy and be certain they are providing you with the correct information.

Fuel filters must be changed and the filter purged of water and residue at regular intervals or they will clog. Oil filters require regular replacement also or they will load up with sludge and restrict the flow of lubricant.

Oil changes are most important for several reasons. The common reason for which many mariners believe they should change the engine oil is the oil will wear out. This is not true. Reclaimed or refiltered oil still retains its lubricating qualities but it has a pair of very real problems.

To begin with, the oil filter never really removes all the particulates which accumulate in the oil. There will be everything from carbon particles to small bits of metal suspended in the oil or lying in the crankcase. The filter gets most but not all of this residue.

When you drain the oil the balance should be retrieved. Always warm the engine first. Get the oil circulating, get those particulates into suspension. Get the oil warm so it will flow easily, then drain the oil. Now most of this harmful residue is removed with the oil.

The second consideration is the detergent package. The

detergent package contains anti-oxidants that assimilate moisture and reduce rusting in the engine. It contains anti-foaming agents to prevent the oil from becoming aerated as the moving parts of the engine bash the lubricant around. There are anti-acids also included.

The burning of gasoline releases five destructive acids in varying amounts and this anti-acid formula renders them harmless for a time. There are other provisions in the detergent package but they vary widely from manufacturer to manufacturer.

The advertisers never agree on what should be in the detergent package or how much should be there but there are three things they do agree upon. First, the presence of the detergents is absolutely necessary. Second, the detergents do wear out. Third, you must change the oil periodically.

If you learn nothing else from this chapter, remember three things: First, speed reduces the life of the engine and great speed greatly reduces the life of the engine. Second, thou shall maintain the engine or it will rebel and punish you. Third, you can still go as fast as your heart desires, if you are willing to pay.

CHAPTER TWENTY-TWO

GRAPHS AND CURVES

The engine manufacturer provides a set of engine specifications which are very useful to the mechanic or boat owner. They include the torque curves, horsepower curves and fuel consumption curves. There are others but these are the ones of greatest interest.

What do we learn from these graphic presentations of engine performance? First let us discuss what these curves are and then move on to their uses. The torque curve has an X and a Y axis with engine rpms displayed along one axis and developed torque along the other.

The horsepower curve has an X and a Y axis with rpms on one axis and horsepower on the other. The fuel curve also has an X and a Y axis with rpms on one of those axes and fuel consumption on the other. Some manufacturers include two or more of these -- torque, horsepower and fuel -- on the same graph.

I will develop the meanings of the different curves separately and then endeavor to show you the interconnected nature of all three. Let us begin with the torque curve.

As we look at the torque curve we will see that developed torque begins at the zero line and increases right along with the growing rpms. This continues throughout the lower rpm ranges. As rpms continue to increase however, the developed torque will finally reach a peak.

After this peak the rpms continue to increase but the developed torque begins to fall off.

At first, it will fall slowly but then as rpms continue to rise, the drop in developed torque becomes quite rapid. This is the result of falling pressure on the piston top.

The induction system has also peaked and it can no longer fully satisfy the demand for air/fuel mix made by the cylinder. It cannot provide the energy to continue the rise in developed torque.

Now look at the horsepower curve. Beginning with the zero point, the horsepower will also increase as the rpms increase. Yet eventually, it too peaks. Peak rpms for the horsepower curve will always come at a higher point in the curve than will developed torque. Why should this be so?

The answer lies in the interconnected relationship between the two. Horsepower is a multiple of factors, torque and rpms. For a time, the rpms will increase at a faster rate than the developed torque falls. Under these conditions, horsepower continues to increase.

This situation cannot continue indefinitely. Finally, as the induction system gets an ever greater demand from the cylinder it will breathe out. Mean effective cylinder pressure becomes ever lower and torque falls off at a rate faster than the rpms are increasing.

From this point on the horsepower too will begin to fall. For a short time horsepower will fall gradually but then as rpms become still higher, it will fall very rapidly indeed.

For how many rpms will the horsepower increase after torque begins to decline? This depends upon engine design; the bore/stroke ratio, camshaft design, carburetion and other factors. What practical lessons can be learned from these curves?

You can deduce several things. Look at the torque curve and see where the torque peak occurs. This is the point of maximum efficiency for the engine. It will also represent your best cruising speed. Take the peak rpms from the torque curve and move over to the horsepower curve.

Looking at the horsepower curve, see how much horsepower is available at the rpms where the torque curve peaked. This is your continuous operating range. The amount of horsepower found at this rpm can be expected from the engine on a day-in-day-out basis.

You are not often concerned with the advertised maximum horsepower figures since you can only use the engine at this speed for short periods of time. Yet there may come a day when you will have to use thefull potential of the engine.

When that emergency does arise, the highest point on the horsepower curve will be the maximum rpms you should turn the engine. It will also be the maximum horsepower available to you. Why turn the engine beyond this point?

When you do so you are losing both horsepower and performance. You are overworking the engine, to no avail. In three words, "Don't do it." Stay within the rpm range that provides maximum horsepower. Get all the power you can and stop.

There is simply no benefit in winding the power plant to greater and greater speeds if there is no increase in horsepower to reward you for doing so. You will consume a great deal of fuel and lose miles per gallon in the bargain. What about the fuel curve?

The fuel curve shows fuel consumed at each rpm increment. It tells us many things.

You should try to have all three curves available when you begin to read. With these at hand, you are ready to balance the fuel consumption against the horsepower produced at any rpm.

This allows you to fine tune your engine operation for the very best performance. The engine will deliver a certain number of horsepower per gallon of fuel. Using fuel consumed and horsepower produced, you can calculate the best operating speed.

This is easy to calculate. Simply divide gallons per hour into horsepower and you will get a figure which we refer to as "gallons per horsepower hour." The engineer generally uses pounds of fuel rather than gallons but gallons will do nicely.

Consider gallons per horsepower hour as an efficiency rating. Estimate that number for each one hundred revolutions on the curve. If you have a flow meter it will be interesting to see how your figures compare with those compiled by the factory.

Factory figures are very close and if you vary from their numbers just a bit, that is acceptable but if you have any large discrepancies you may have a problem with the engine. This is a wake-up call.

There is a great deal of good information in these curves. Torque curves, horsepower curves, fuel consumption curves, all tell their own story. If you did not understand either mechanical or mathematical explanations above, at least understand the curves.

Know torque rises and falls with the rpms. Horsepower rises and falls with the rpms but at a different rate. Remember, the engine is most efficient at the rpms where the torque curve peaks.

Know the rpms at which the torque curve peaks is also your continuous operating range and the point at which the horsepower curve peaks is the maximum horsepower available, regardless of how fast you turn engine.

See how torque, horsepower and rpms relate to fuel consumption and if you only master these things, you are well paid.

We are going to do a section on high performance. It will indeed be abbreviated and devoted principally to supercharging but this is an ever-growing field and any serious treatise on the subject of engines should not ignore the supercharger.

CHAPTER TWENTY-THREE

PARTS & ACCESSORIES

Accessories for the gasoline powered, marine engine are certainly not automotive parts. They should not be confused with automotive parts and they must never be substituted for them. An interchange between automotive parts and marine parts can be a disaster.

The marine carburetor has an extra vacuum port inset into its body. This port is noticeable because of the small hose barb or nipple which protrudes from the carburetor body to access the vacuum port. The nipple is about 1/8th-inch, inside diameter.

The hose from this nipple extends downward to the fuel pump body at the base of the engine block. It joins a similar nipple affixed to the top of the fuel pump. This nipple enters the pump body at a point above the diaphragm.

Should the diaphragm develop a leak the fuel could puddle on top of the diaphragm and eventually find its way into the bilge of the boat. The vacuum from the carburetor draws this fuel up into the manifold and burns it harmlessly.

Without this safety feature on both parts, carburetor and fuel pump, a leak at the fuel pump diaphragm could easily have a disastrous result. Automotive carburetors and automotive fuel pumps do not have this feature and, on a boat, they are essential.

Distributors for the marine engine have a gasket around the distributor cap which keeps fumes from the crankcase out of the distributor and away from the almost continuous sparks that are occurring inside the cap. They also have gauze over the ventilator port on the distributor body.

The distributor makes ozone when it fires. Ozone is that smell you get when lightning strikes during a thunderstorm. Ozone is highly corrosive and without this ventilator port the inside of the distributor would become corroded. The gauze also helps to keep fumes out of the distributor.

Automotive distributors do not have the gasket on the cap nor the gauze covered ventilation holes in the body. They can easily flash any fumes in the bilge. Fumes and sparks in the bilge are poor companions.

Alternators for the marine engine are totally enclosed and explosion proof. These are designations with which any electrician is familiar. They refer to the fact that any opening which might expose the internal elements of the alternator to bilge fumes has been covered in some way. The marine alternator should be quite safe in the bilges.

The marine starter is totally enclosed and explosion proof also. This accessory does not operate for more than a few seconds but a single spark can be enough. Do not buy automotive starters for your boat. The savings are not worth the risk.

Marine switches have provisions to shield them from any kind of fumes found aboard your vessel. A switch only makes a small spark and then only on few occasions but once again, it only takes one spark to do the job.

Why do the marine parts cost so much? The popular answer to this question is, "Oh, it's just for a boat and they make everything expensive for boats because they know we will pay it." The truth is a bit different. Product insurance for these marine parts is high and higher.

This should tell you a couple of things. First, the

manufacturer believes the danger is real and considering how much he pays for insurance he must also believe that he needs it. The second thing is if the manufacturer is willing to pay this enormous cost, you had better accept his judgment and buy marine.

These are the safety considerations but there are some differences between automotive and marine parts that have to do with longevity and fitness for the special purpose. A couple of examples are the water pump and the cylinder head gasket.

Marine water pumps have a stainless steel shaft instead of the ferrous metal shaft on the automotive water pump. The seal is made of non corrosive materials and the pump will function well in saltwater. An automotive pump will not do so.

The cylinder head gasket is a special item for marine applications. It has stainless steel or copper sealing rings around all the water openings and cylinder bores. There have been many different types of head gasket used over the years, but I have never seen an automotive gasket I would want to interchange for a marine part.

The camshaft is a special item. It provides a broad torque band which is ideal for marine use. The marine engine has only one gear in which to run and one chance to tailor needed torque to a wide range of needs.

How about the internal parts of the engine? Don Weiderhold was the engineer in charge of the Special Products Division of General Motors before that group became known as "Power Train." Since Special Products Division was building the marine block, I asked that question of him.

This is not a quote but it is the gist of what he said. Marine engine manufacturers might be better described as "Marinizers." They buy a basic marine block assembly from Chevrolet Motor Company. This engine is a heavy duty unit with premium parts.

The marine engine runs under a continuous load. There are no hills to coast down and little opportunity for the engine to rest. The marine engine must stand up under constant stress and he designed the marine engine for this severe service.

To this basic engine, the marinizers add their own parts and pieces. Intake manifolds are usually Chevrolet parts. Chevrolet engines have shown good results with Rochester Carburetors but that choice lies with the marinizer.

Exhaust manifolds are usually proprietary castings furnished by the marinizer. Accessories are furnished by the marinizer and they may or may not be Chevrolet parts. Some manufacturers buy less than complete engines and add special parts of their own choosing.

Mercury Marine is an example of a high performance builder who buys some partial engines from Chevrolet and adds other parts of their own design to that engine. I asked Don, "Just how big is Chevrolet in the marine field?"

The answer came in 1991 and at that time Chevrolet sold 88 percent of the gasoline powered marine engines, worldwide. This is total domination in any field (my statement, not from Chevrolet) and nobody can hold that much business in a highly competitive field unless they are doing something right.

The figure may be slightly greater today. Buy a Volvo Marine Engine and you will almost certainly get a Chevrolet. How about Crusader or Marine Power? Same story, they are Chevrolets also. This is not a bad thing at all, for the Chevrolet marine engine is rock solid dependable.

Besides which, this saturation of one brand engines means parts are easy to find and many parts are in stock on a dealer's shelf. The Chevrolet marine engine is like a twelve gauge shotgun, you can get shells for it at any hardware store.

CHAPTER TWENTY-FOUR

THE SUPERCHARGER

This chapter is really for the performance buffs among you but it contains some valuable insights into the world of engines. In this chapter you will learn how a blower or supercharger can change the engines characteristics in dramatic fashion, creates high horsepower -- at a cost.

Gasoline engines may be normally aspirated or blown. The normally aspirated engine uses the pressure of the atmosphere to charge the engine's cylinder. The supercharged engine uses an air compressor to force air into the engine. We call this air compressor a supercharger or blower.

The supercharger can feed large amounts of air/fuel mix into the engine's cylinder. In fact, there is little limit to how much air/fuel mix we can get into the cylinders with a blower but there is a limit to how much the engine can accept without destroying itself.

Let us begin with a bit of mathematics. Remember the horsepower formula we used before?

$$P \times L \times A \times N / 33{,}000 = \text{Horsepower}$$

How does the supercharger fit in?

Look at the factors involved. We are not going to increase the cubic displacement, thus L and A remain the same. If we want to increase the horsepower we have P and N to work with. The most fertile area for any accessory which produces pressure is P or Mean Effective Cylinder Pressure.

This is where the blower shines. When we produce engines for the local hot boaters we want some small amount of longevity. The engine will not live very long when you double or triple its original horsepower but it will produce scintillating horsepower numbers.

It will also produce gobs of torque. We usually increase the engine rpms by 1,500 or less in going from 385 horsepower to 850 horsepower, on a 502 cubic-inch Chevrolet block. The engine originally turned 4,450 in its normally aspirated form.

Figure 15

This 502 cubic inch engine shows the stout rocker arms necessary for a supercharged engine. This is only one area of concern when a blower is added.

If we are not going to change the displacement and the rpms are only going up a bit. Where is the horsepower coming from? In a word, pressure. High pressure and high torque go together since that increase in cylinder pressure translates into increased force on the crankshaft arm.

This all sounds wonderful. The blower is comparatively cheap when measured against the cost per horsepower. Why not supercharge everything? The rub comes in the form of heat or cylinder temperature, if you prefer. High pressures create lots of heat.

As these temperatures grow, detonation sets in, pistons and rings fail, valves burn and the engine may incinerate itself. Let us do another bit of math here and consider the matter of compression pressures. There is a formula for this:

$$V1 : V2 : P1 : P2$$

In this model we see volume one, the total volume of the cylinder is to volume two, the volume of the combustion chamber alone, as pressure one, (usually atmospheric) is to pressure two. Pressure one in a normally aspirated engine is 14.7 pounds at sea level, assuming 100 percent cylinder charge.

Let us assume a total cylinder content, including the combustion chamber, is 100 cubic inches. Let us further assume the combustion chamber has a volume of 12 cubic inches and the initial pressure in the cylinder is 14.7 $lbs./in.^2$. Now put these numbers into the formula 100 : 12 : 14.7 : X.

The cylinder pressure should be 122.499 $lbs./in.^2$. It will be higher in actual practice because of heat expansion as the engine compresses but let us stay with the simple math. The results are certainly representative of what is happening in the engine.

Okay, the blower produces boost. This is a positive pressure, above atmospheric and it is measured by a boost gauge. Let us assume the boost gauge is running at 8 $lbs./in.^2$.

and the engine has the same dimensions as above.

Add those eight pounds of boost to the atmospheric pressure and proceed as before. We now have 100 : 12 : 22.7 : X and the cylinder pressure should be 189.159 lbs./in.^{2}. The boost has raised our pressure by more than 50 per cent without even allowing for heat expansion, as in the first model.

How does this relate to engine operation. One way is in the matter of fuel and octane rating. The fuel you once ran is good for that 122 lbs./in.^{2}. compression pressure but how will it react to 189 lbs./in.^{2}? In a word, Violently.

Remember, when we ignite the fuel, pressures will rise rapidly, even on the lower compression pressure. At the higher compression pressure it will grow at a tremendous rate. The flame front will spread very rapidly, indeed.

A blower has the same effect as drastically increasing compression pressures, as if you had raised the compression ratio. Your fuel octane rating must change accordingly. When boost reaches numbers above 10 lbs./in.^{2} you may have to consider a racing fuel.

Most, if not all, blown engines run in at least mild detonation, a good percentage of the time. Detonation is harmful to the engine and interior parts are subjected to excessive heat and pressure. This is actually going on to one degree or another, even when the engine is running right."

The 2,000 hour marine engine is a good one if it lasts 100 (yeah, one hundred) hours. The stern drive will enjoy a like fate when operated behind a supercharged engine. The life of this assembly is drastically shortened by the effects of a blower.

The target we shoot for is 100 hours of engine operation and 30 to 40 one-minute runs against your buddy or one of the out of town crowd. Note the time element. If you hold those races to one minute each you are going to do fairly well but never, ever, try holding that baby wide open for any length of time.

Lubrication is a problem with the supercharged engine

and blow-by is aggravated as well. Blow-by is the amount of hot gasses that sneak by the piston rings during engine operation. There will always be a certain amount of leakage by the rings.

In stock engines this is nominal, if the engine is in good shape but it will increase as the engine wears. On the blown engine it is considerable even when the engine is new. This blow-by heats the oil and tends to reduce its lubricating qualities. It also contaminates the lubricant.

Try to keep the oil temperature to less than 250 degrees on the supercharged engine. Always have a temperature gauge on the crankcase oil and always have an adequate heat exchanger to cool it.

I have said so many negative things about the supercharged engine you might get the idea I do not like them. Quite the opposite is true. The answer lies in a quotation from the eulogy read at the funeral of the late Marilyn Monroe. It came from the pen of Edna St. Vincent Millay and it goes like this:

> "My candle burns at both ends;
> It will not last the night.
> But ah, my foes and oh, my friends
> It gives a lovely light."

The blown engine is like a bright light, illuminating that shining world of speed but it burns for only a short time.

CHAPTER TWENTY-FIVE

THE REBUILD

We often get so deep into electronics and technology we forget the basic engine and the mechanical skills necessary to rebuild it. I want to begin with carburetors and accessories, then move on to the heavy stuff. I always use an exploded view for any carburetor.

The exploded view comes with the rebuild kit. Lay the paper out on the bench and disassemble the carburetor, piece by piece. Lay it out exactly like the exploded view. Never mind about inspecting the parts until they are all laid out on the bench.

Take out the old parts, one at a time. Replace the old parts with the new ones, one at a time. Discard the old parts only after the new ones are in place. Now reassemble in the reverse order, as the exploded view shows. It really is that simple.

Most accessories, starters, alternators, etc. can be bought from a reliable rebuilder cheaper and easier than you can do a rebuild yourself. You get a good part with a guarantee you do not have to back with your own money.

The basic engine is actually an easy rebuild but you must pay attention to detail. Begin with disassembly. Take each piece off the engine, one part at a time and put the bolts in freezer baggies, labeled with their purpose. Lay the parts out as you remove them.

The crankshaft should always be stood on end. Never lay it flat, it will warp. In building an opposite rotation engine set I always place the engines in separate areas of the shop in the manner in which they go in the boat. Never commingle the parts.

Now measure everything. The pistons, skirt to wall clearance, crankshaft (rods and mains), camshaft lobes and journals, valve guides, valve stems and the rod alignment. Take everything that is outside of factory specification to the machine shop.

Always have the machine shop vat or boil the heads and block to clean them but do not stop there. When you have the engine back in your own hands remove the threaded plugs from the oil galleries and take a rifle brush to clean these passages.

Replace the camshaft bearings with every overhaul and if you are not confident in this undertaking, get the machine shop to install a set for you. Do not automatically go to a .030 oversize on the cylinder bore or a .020 undersize on the crankshaft.

If the crankshaft can be polished only or simply ground to a .002 undersized bearing, do it. If the cylinder bores will clean at .010, do that. Never remove more metal than necessary, you may want to build this engine again and you will need metal to do so.

I like a light cross hatch, done with a 600 grit hone on the cylinder walls. You can talk to the machine shop or consult the ring manufacturer.

When you have the valves reground and the seats renewed, try to remove as little metal as possible. The valve seats sink into the cylinder heads with grinding and the valves follow. They become shrouded by the surrounding metal, the engine loses air flow and consequently loses horsepower.

Always have the valve springs checked for tension and shimmed if necessary. Always buy marine parts for any replacements and be certain you are buying for the proper engine rotation.

An example? The front crankshaft seal. We commonly refer to this as the "timing cover seal" and it is one source of real trouble for the rebuilder. These seals have striations across their face with an angle of attack against the direction of crankshaft rotation. If they are facing in the proper direction they tend to pull oil off the face of the seal and back into the engine.

On the other hand, if they are facing the wrong way they can empty the crankcase into the bilge in a matter of hours. The mechanic has little room for error in the assembly of the engine and even less when pairs are involved.

Another area of concern is freeze plugs. Always use brass freeze plugs on the marine engine. If you skimp here you are making a real mistake. Those on the sides of the engine can cause problems but the plug at the camshaft on the rear of the block can force the removal of the engine if it fails. All for a $2.00 plug.

When you are ready to reassemble the engine, take the bolts out of the baggies and inspect them carefully. If the heads are worn or rusted, replace them. If the threads are even slightly damaged, replace them. If you are going to reuse them, buff them clean on a wire wheel, wash them in a vat and oil them lightly. Put them back in the labeled baggie.

Chase all thread holes in the block with a good quality tap and be certain that the bolts run free in those holes. If the bolts are tight in the holes the torque wrench will not give a true reading. Install the rings into the cylinder bores and check the end gaps with a feeler gauge. File the gaps to fit, if necessary.

Turn the pistons upside down in the cylinder bores and check the skirt to wall clearance. Sure, the machine shop just finished with the engine and they do great work but anyone can make a mistake. Now is the time to find out.

Use a marine gasket set and reassemble everything

exactly in the order established in the service manual.

When the engine and all its parts are sanitary clean, I always mount the crankshaft first. I have never seen a service manual that called for a different procedure. Install the bearings in the main caps and the block webbings, place a strip of Plasti-Gauge across each bearing and torque the caps down with clean and lightly oiled bolts.

Remove the caps and check the Plasti-Gauge. If the Plasti-Gauge shows that the bearing clearance is correct, clean the bearing and coat it liberally with a good quality grease. Reinstall the caps. Torque all bolts down to factory specifications in the proper sequence, stopping frequently to be certain the crankshaft rotates freely.

Install the rings on the piston/rod assembly and space the end gaps according to the method detailed on the package. Take care to get the rings in the right groove. This is important. Improper ring installation can cause the engine to burn oil.

Liberally coat the piston, rings and cylinder bore with single viscosity oil and cover the rod bolts with a short length of rubber tube. The rubber tube will prevent the bolts from damaging the crankshaft during installation. Use a good quality ring compressor.

Tap, do not hammer the piston to get it to enter the cylinder bore. If your ring compressor is properly installed, very little pressure will be necessary. If you use a lot of pressure you may well break a ring.

Install the pistons, one at a time, with Plasti-Gauge across the rod bearings. Torque them down, remove the caps and check for clearance. Clearance okay? Clean the bearing, grease liberally with a good quality grease and torque the rod down. Now rotate the engine.

When you have the crankshaft and rod assembly in place you can mount the oil pan and install the cylinder heads. I am willing to use a sealer on the crankcase gasket if you really want one but leave it off the cylinder head gasket.

Be certain the cylinder heads are torqued exactly according to factory specifications and in the proper sequence. I have been building engines for many years but I still use a helper with the service manual in his hands to designate the next bolt to tighten and how tight to pull it. Sound amateurish? Maybe you never made a mistake.

This is not everything there is to know about engine rebuild but it is a good start. Use caution, pay attention to detail and keep it clean. The tools, the engine, the whole thing must be clean. The Bible says, “Cleanliness is next to Godliness,” and nowhere is this more true than in the engine itself.

IGNITION SYSTEMS

We are about to delve into a subject that can be as simple or as complicated as you wish to make it. I will try to do this the easy way. The ignition system consists of a coil, a distributor, a set of spark plug wires and a set of spark plugs.

There are two common systems, the conventional system and the electronic system. Each system employs a distributor. The distributor is a device which literally distributes a spark to the various cylinders, in order. Inside the distributor is a rotor.

The rotor is mounted on the distributor shaft and rotates with the shaft. It has a sort of finger which points to conductors spaced evenly around the cap. High tension electricity jumps the gap between the rotor and distributor cap. It then enters the plug wires.

Both systems employ a coil which is nothing more than a transformer. The transformer changes low voltage current with high amperage to high voltage current with low amperage. We need this high voltage to jump the gap on the spark plugs.

Up to this point, the conventional and electronic

ignition systems appear very similar but from this point on, they differ widely.

Follow along. The conventional ignition system employs a set of contact points. They are nothing more than a switch.

The presence of these points gives rise to the term "make and break" which is sometimes applied to these systems. The points make and break a circuit which delivers current to the primary side of the coil.

When the points close, low voltage current from the storage battery is fed to the coil. The coil has a soft iron core and a primary or low tension winding. The low tension winding consists of a few turns of wire around the soft iron core.

When the points close, the primary circuit is saturated with electrons. We have established an electromagnetic field.

The high voltage circuit consists of a secondary or high tension winding. This high tension winding employs numerous turns of wire, many more than in the primary winding. There is no direct contact between the primary and secondary windings. In fact, they are insulated from each other with a kind of baked on varnish.

As the distributor shaft turns, a cam or eccentric on the shaft will open the points. The circuit is broken and the magnetic field collapses. All of the stored up energy in the coil has to go somewhere and it does. It enters the secondary winding through what is known as induction. Induced current is a process somewhat like osmosis.

The secondary winding multiplies the voltage in that induced current many times and delivers a high voltage spark to the distributor. The distributor, in turn, delivers the spark to the plug wires and thence to the spark plug.

The electronic ignition still uses a coil which operates just like the one on the conventional ignition system but it has no points. The electronic system uses a capacitor or condenser to store current from the battery. A transistor which can be considered a valve or switch replaces the ignition points.

Inside the distributor you will need some type of trigger device. This device can be electrical magnetic or it can employ a light beam. The magnetic system has a module which consists of a small coil mounted on the flat plate and the rotor is fitted with a magnet.

When the rotor magnet passes across the coil in the module, a small pulse develops in the module and trips or releases the stored up current in the capacitor. This capacitor discharge gives rise to the term "capacitive discharge ignition." The current from the capacitor is delivered to the low tension side of the coil. From this point on, the coil function resembles a conventional ignition. The distributor is triggered by a light beam is different only in terms of how it provides the trigger effect.

This system uses a narrow beam of light with a light sensor to trip the transistor. When the light beam strikes the sensor it signals the transistor to deliver current from the capacitor to the primary winding in the coil.

Now the process becomes quite similar to the operation of the conventional system but there are still some differences. The conventional ignition system can only receive 12 volts from the battery to the low tension winding in the coil.

The system may even use a resistor to lower that input voltage to 6 volts. This is done to help keep arcing of the ignition points to a minimum and extend their life. Then there is the matter of coil saturation. As the rpms increase, the amount of time available between firing sequences is reduced accordingly.

The primary circuit in the coil has less time to saturate and the voltage at the secondary is reduced. At top rpms, when you need it most, the spark is beginning to fade. At low rpms a conventional system will typically deliver about 20,000 volts, dropping to as little as 4,000 volts at the top end.

The electronic distributor has no such problem. It receives much higher voltage at the primary winding when the capacitor discharges itself into the primary. This system can deliver from 40,000 volts to 50,000 volts and maintain this delivery rate all the way to 10,000 rpms.

Thus the electronic ignition system has higher voltage, over a greater rpm range and it requires much less maintenance. The transistor will outlast a set of points, many times over.

The last comparison is in terms of control and in this area the electronic ignition stands alone.

The conventional distributor employs a set of weights and springs to provide its spark advance and retard. These weights operate on centrifugal force and the rate of change in the spark timing is not too precise. With the electronic distributor the process is computer controlled and it is near perfect.

The last comparison truly leaves the electronic distributor as the only choice. The ECM or Electronic Control Module has overall control of all systems on the modern engine. It tailors spark timing to engine load and fuel from the injectors to the needs of the engine. It receives input from sensors located about the engine and coordinates the operation of all these systems for optimum performance. There is no other method that offers such an integrated control of the engine. The conventional distributor has no potential for this capability.

If the modern era had not produced anything but an electronic ignition system, it would have done at least one great thing, for this system is almost bulletproof.

DIAGNOSTICS, TROUBLE SHOOTING & PROBLEM SOLVING

Diagnostics is the most difficult job facing the medical doctor and it is also the most difficult job facing the engine tech. Virtually any doctor can treat the patient if they can diagnose the problem. Not every doctor can make the correct diagnosis.

The engine tech can easily repair your engine if he can properly diagnose the problem. Not every engine tech can do this and so diagnostics is perhaps the most important ability the engine tech can possess.

Today, much of our diagnosis is done by a laptop computer but there is no instrument that will replace human intelligence. You should begin any career as a mechanic by learning to diagnose the problems in the engine. This chapter will only scratch the surface.

I want to begin with the principal requirements for engine operation. Every engine must have five elementary things available in order to run.

1. A combustible fuel
2. Mixed with air in the proper proportions
3. Compression
4. A proper source of ignition
5. All provided at the correct time

Every problem the trouble shooter will encounter will result from the loss or failure of one or more of these elements. Diagnosis must begin with no preconceptions. You must not decide what is wrong with the engine before you have the facts to go on.

Begin your trouble shooting efforts with an open mind but try to quickly categorize the problem. Try to isolate it into one or more of those areas listed above. By doing this you quickly narrow your search to a smaller number of parts or pieces.

You save a great deal of time that might be wasted looking for theproblem in the wrong place. Perhaps this sounds a bit too simple but it is not. It is a logical procedure.

Think about the things that have gone wrong with your engines over the years. No matter what was described as the problem with those engines, every one of those problems fits into one or more of the categories listed here.

In this book we have detailed each of the systems that help the engine to function. The systems which in fact do provide those vital elements listed above. Carburetors, injectors, ignition systems etc. We have tied each of those systems into the total operation of the engine and described the operation of each of them.

In the future you should be able to look at any engine, make a few checks and know the area in which your problem lies. I cannot overemphasize the importance of this elimination process. With mechanic's time-billed at a record high, the mechanic must be able to isolate those problems quickly.

By placing the problem in a specific category and by understanding which parts are utilized within that category, the diagnostician knows immediately which part or group of parts are suspect. Let me give you an example.

If your engine suddenly stops during operation you will first make two checks. Check for fuel at the carburetor and a spark at the plugs. If either of these are missing, consider the possible source of the problem. Assume that there is no fuel at the carburetor.

The fuel pump, fuel lines, fuel filter, fuel tank pick up and fuel supply are the likely sources of your problem. You now have a quick list of the potential sources of your trouble and you have narrowed your search to an easily managed area.

Assume there is no spark. The parts involved in the production of a spark are the battery, the battery switch, the wiring harness, the ignition switch, the coil, the distributor, the plug wires and the plugs themselves.

The part or parts needed to restore a proper spark are somewhere in this group. You do not know exactly which of these parts to blame for your troubles but you do know where to look and this can save a great deal of time.

Mechanical repair is one thing but problem solving is an entirely separate function and it is a very important subject for anyone to master. It extends to many areas beyond simple breakdown. I lump propeller selection, fuel type, lubrication type, spark plug selection, maintenance intervals and numerous other decisions into this category.

When you have developed a greater understanding of engine operation you may begin to make decisions for yourself. Do I need closer maintenance intervals than the factory recommends? Is my oil doing well? Are my spark plugs too hot/cold? How good is my propeller?

All of these things are important and you must understand the elements of diagnostics in order to be able to solve the problems of everyday engine performance. You cannot hope to improve that which you do not understand.

Much of the information which you need to trouble shoot an engine is contained within the pages of the service manual and this should be your Bible but it is not a license to relax and play dumb. You must be involved with the engine if you are ever going to be a really good mechanic. You will eat, sleep, breathe and even dream about engines.

When the engine has become a living part of you, only then will you truly understand.

Buying A Great Boat
Written By Arthur Edmunds

Outfitting & Organizing Your Boat For A Day, A Week or A Lifetime
Written By Michael L. Frankel

Boater's Book of Nautical Terms
Written By David S. Yetman

Modern Boatworks
Written By David S. Yetman

Practical Seamanship
Written By David S. Yetman

Captain Jack's Basic Navigation
Written By Jack I. Davis

Captain Jack's Celestial Navigation
Written By Jack I. Davis

Captain Jack's Complete Navigation
Written By Jack I. Davis

Southwinds Gourmet
Written By Susan Garrett Mason

The Cruising Sailor
Written By Tom Dove

Daddy & I Go Boating
Written By Ken Kreisler

My Grandpa Is A Tugboat Captain
Written By Ken Kreisler

Billy The Oysterman
Written By Ken Kreisler

Creating Comfort Afloat
Written By Janet Groene

Living Aboard
Written By Janet Groene

Simple Boat Projects
Written By Donald Boone

Racing The Ice To Cape Horn
Written By Frank Guernsey & Cy Zoerner

Boater's Checklist
Written By Clay Kelley

Florida Through The Islands
What Boaters Need To Know
Written By Captain Clay Kelley & Marybeth

Marine Weather Forecasting
Written By J. Frank Brumbaugh

Basic Boat Maintenance
Written By J. Frank Brumbaugh

Complete Guide To Gasoline Marine Engines
Written By John Fleming

Complete Guide To Outboard Engines
Written By John Fleming

Complete Guide To Diesel Marine Engines
Written By John Fleming

Trouble Shooting Gasoline Marine Engines
Written By John Fleming

Trailer Boats
Written By Alex Zidock

Skipper's Handbook
Written By Robert S. Grossman

Wake Up & Water Ski
Written By Kimberly P. Robinson

White Squall - The Last Voyage Of Albatross
Written By Richard E. Langford

Cruising South
What to Expect Along The ICW
Written By Joan Healy

Electronics Aboard
Written By Stephen Fishman

A Whale At the Port Quarter
A Treasure Chest of Sea Stories
Written By Charles Gnaegy

Five Against The Sea
A True Story of Courage & Survival
Written By Ron Arias

Scuttlebutt
Seafaring History & Lore
Written By Captain John Guest USCG Ret.

Cruising The South Pacific
Written By Douglas Austin

After Forty Years
How To Avoid The Pitfalls of Boating
Written By David Wheeler

Catch of The Day
How To Catch, Clean & Cook It
Written By Carla Johnson

REVIEWS

Southern Boating - Jerry Renninger

Somewhere in this solar system there's probably an individual who knows as much about marine engines as John Fleming, but if so, it's doubtful that he writes with equal clarity on this highly technical and complex subject.

Mark Klossner - Mercury Marine
Dealer Training Manager, Mercury University

"Bravo to John Fleming for translating the technical jargon of marine propulsion in a way that's easy for everyone to understand. His three books, *Complete Guide To Outboard Engines, Complete Guide To Gasoline Marine Engines,* and *Complete Guide To Diesel Marine Engines* are well-written, thoughtfully laid out and very informative. They should be required reading for anyone who owns, fixes or sells marine engines!"